CANCER

& Other Things
I'm Grateful For

In good health,

Erika K. Wolf

CANCER

& Other Things I'm Grateful For

How Self-Advocacy and Integrative Medicine Led to Holistic Healing

Erika K. Wolf

BOOKLOGIX

Alpharetta, Georgia

ISBN: 978-1-6653-0612-6 - Paperback
eISBN: 978-1-6653-0613-3 - ePub

Library of Congress Control Number: 2023908040

☉This paper meets the requirements of ANSI/NISO Z39.48-1992
(Permanence of Paper)

Author photo by Danielle Batchelor

0 5 0 1 2 3

To my entire dream team,
especially Michael, Aspen, Zach, and Kerrianne,
for all you did to get me to where I am today.

Contents

Preface

Cancer and Other Things I'm Grateful For is my personal account of my breast cancer diagnosis, treatment, and subsequent effects, based on a blog I started to process the experience. At the nerve center is the complementary care I sought which led to more complete healing and filled the conspicuous gaps in traditional oncology medicine.

One of yogic philosopher B. K. S. Iyengar's most famous teachings offers, "Yoga teaches us to cure what need not be endured and endure what cannot be cured."

I lived by his philosophy throughout my cancer treatment. Whenever I came to a turning point and needed grounding, I meditated on his saying and integrated its truth.

I chose radical acceptance when it came to being handed a diagnosis of stage III breast cancer. At the same time, I chose to give myself permission to pursue alternative treatments and believe in the power of the mind-body connection because, even though I was in pain, I did not have to suffer.

I chose to express gratitude, not in the hopes of forgetting my diagnosis but to shift my focus to what was going right, what was in my favor, and what I already had.

I am sharing my story for others to see how we can empower ourselves to own our paths on our health journeys, whether that involves questioning authority, switching from a doctor that doesn't meld with us, or illuminating our own approach to overcoming a major challenge. We are our own best advocates.

Introduction

These days, my life is overflowing with gratitude. Any day that my gratitude outweighs my expectations is a good day. I feel grateful for my two kids, my husband, my family, my friends, and my dogs. I feel grateful for oatmilk lattes, warm coats, contact lenses, chocolate, the ability to hike, ski, and run—and for cancer.

Really? Yep, cancer.

Throughout my long journey of treatment, I found a way to invite radical acceptance into my life and began recognizing the power in choosing my responses to circumstances seemingly beyond my control.

But it didn't start off that way.

Day One

My commute to work was short those days—just a few miles— but it's one of the most gorgeous drives I've ever done. Through the canyon, past the hogback, down to the reservoir, and right into my boss's neighborhood. Every time I drove that path, I drank it in and relished the natural beauty. But on that one cold, sunny weekday morning in December of 2014, I barely noticed.

My mind was totally preoccupied that day, as it had been for weeks. On autopilot, I popped into my boss's house and got busy focusing on my daily routine of prepping for the upcoming weekend's events.

Within just a few minutes, my phone rang. I snapped to attention and held my breath as I checked who was calling.

It was the call; the one I'd been waiting for. I answered as fast as I could. The suspense of the past six weeks had been excruciating.

The conversation was short—maybe a minute and a half. But I heard what I needed to hear from the radiologist: the biopsy was malignant. I hadn't wanted bad news; I just knew it was coming. We hung up, and it was official.

I had cancer.

The doctors finally knew what I had already known deep in my heart. I knew because the pain and swelling from the mass in my left breast had been a ceaseless reminder. I knew because life had become a daunting cycle of doctor's appointments: Test. Wait. Repeat. I knew because the conversations were absent of any reassuring platitudes or smiles of relief. I knew because there was seriousness. And scheduling.

To get more answers, I went from breast exam and thermogram to ultrasound, mammogram, MRI, and finally, biopsy. With each step, I digested the reality a little bit more: Something is wrong. Let's learn more.

So there, I had it—a definitive diagnosis.

I didn't panic or freak out. I didn't even cry. Not then, anyway. After all of the talking and tests and waiting, I was utterly relieved to know. I had something to go on. Answers. Finally.

Shaken, but energized, I told the news to my boss (who already knew the call was anticipated any day), hopped in my car, and drove the beautiful route, once again, back home. This time on the drive, I called my nephew Aaron—the first of many calls to him—who is a pathologist at one of the best-known hospital systems in the country. I gave him the information I had, and he was very empathetic, but moreover, he was invaluable. He prompted me to ask key questions that I didn't know I needed to know: What type of cancer is it? What stage is it? What grade is it? I hung up with a list of questions that lit a fire under my ass. And I was off.

While I had been waiting the previous six weeks, I had time to start preparing myself for this possibility. I had the support of my husband, my family, and close friends. But I also needed to develop a list of doctors to interview. I needed to understand my insurance benefits. I needed to identify what to eat, learn how to prepare my body, and fathom what lie ahead. So, I began reading everything I could track down about breast cancer, treatment, and care. And now that I irrevocably had a confirmed diagnosis, I could put all of this material to use. I could get the wheels in motion, selecting a medical team, investigating how to treat the disease, and seeking answers to a whole new list of questions. To say I was eager is an understatement.

Unfortunately, it was only a matter of hours before I found myself right back in the familiar cycle: Test. Wait. Repeat.

I was scared and wanted to start fixing the problem *now*. But the calmer, more rational part of me understood that knowing the details of my situation was crucial to assembling a care team, formulating a plan, and choosing the best course of treatment.

We had a few pieces of the puzzle in place, but we needed to know more: What type? What grade? What stage? Were there genetic mutations? Had it spread to any other organs? And so on. For about three more weeks, I plowed through mammograms, MRIs, X-rays, a PET scan, and countless consultations. Each step brought some answers, but also more questions. I felt both encouraged and frustrated. I was anxious but relieved to be in the process. I was both dealing with it and not yet dealing with it at the same time.

During this second waiting period, I faced the heinous task of sharing the news with all those who are important to me—my parents, my seven siblings, countless nieces, nephews, cousins, aunts, uncles, and in-laws, my very close and lifelong friends, coworkers, neighbors, a close group of social media friends, and most significantly, my kids, who were then sixteen and thirteen.

A common theme from those conversations was that this wasn't supposed to happen to *me*. After all, I was forty-three years old. A runner, a yogi, a former wellness coach. Someone who grows herbs and vegetables, cooks meals from scratch, and tries to live a balanced life. I wasn't *supposed* to get cancer.

But cancer doesn't discriminate like that.

Yes, poor lifestyle habits can contribute to an increased risk, as can family history and a whole list of environmental factors. But thinking "Why *me*?" was not going to help.

After telling everyone, I was swamped by texts, emails, and phone calls offering help and support. People wanted to know the next steps and details. Others wanted to share their experiences or advice.

I was beyond appreciative and immeasurably happy to have help, but the sheer volume was overwhelming. I wished that everyone could somehow magically know everything I knew to that point and everything that was to come without having to exhaust myself reliving the story on repeat every single day. I started losing my voice from all the talking. I was struggling to keep track of whom I had told what. I was quickly running out of steam.

That's when the idea for a blog was born; I needed a way to communicate en masse. I started writing four days after I got the diagnosis and invited my friends and family to follow along. As the days accumulated and the information poured in from my doctors, I could type it all out—once—and then allow it to sink in for myself.

It was a great mode of communication to tell a complex and personal story to the people who care about me from coast to coast and across the seas to the Netherlands, Germany, Ireland, and beyond, but it ripened into so much more than that.

In Treatment

Twenty-three days after the initial diagnosis, I got my first infusion of chemotherapy. It was December 26, 2014. The eighteen-plus months that followed were consumed by my treatment, recovery, and return to "normal" life. It was painful at times. Boring at others. Exhilarating, even, now and then. And sometimes, it was heartbreaking.

But I don't wish the call never came. I don't spend time wishing that none of it happened.

In fact, I became grateful that it did.

Am I crazy? Not at all. I am boundlessly happy and perpetually grateful for where I am in my life today. And because that's true, how could I not be grateful for *everything* that got me here?

Cancer is a physical disease to be sure, but in parallel with that, it is infinitely more. Cancer affects every part of a person's being — the emotional/mental element, the spiritual element, relationships, and even finances. It changed me in ways I couldn't have seen coming, and my life is more abundant, open, and free for having been planted at these crossroads.

Throughout the course of two years and 160-plus blog posts, my body underwent chemotherapy, a bilateral mastectomy, radiation, and reconstructive surgery, which were all indispensable and, thankfully, successful. However, it was the complementary care that I received from my integrative medicine specialist, my physical therapist, my yoga instructors, and my psychotherapist and others that provided me with unforeseen yet priceless breakthroughs, discoveries, and growth that changed my life — that changed *me*.

The oncology treatments were unavoidably front and center, and rightfully so. Oncology specialists must focus their concern on disease eradication, which is obviously the vital main objective. However, this is often done at the expense of overlooking, or even discounting, complementary therapies that treat the whole person — therapies like acupuncture, herbs, physical therapy, yoga, lymphatic drainage, massage, and psychotherapy. It is positive mental, spiritual, and emotional healing unified with a comprehensive approach to treating the entire body that makes enduring the rigors of oncology therapies even possible. To focus solely on the cancer, while ignoring (or even stripping) the rest of a person's complete wellness, is not a full recovery.

This unique blend of traditional therapies coupled with Eastern complementary care led me to radical acceptance of what was happening — to accept this experience as if I'd chosen it. I'll write that phrase again: *accept this experience as if I'd chosen it.* It was infinitely less burdensome to successfully get through this inevitable circumstance because I wasn't constantly wishing it weren't happening.

I was relieved of that tremendous weight thanks to the insight of my therapist. She taught me that the best time to get everything

I could from this experience was while I was in the midst of it. So, I took her advice, and with it, I began to look at experiences as lessons with something to be learned or gained. Throughout my treatment, I saw both the best and worst in people, the world, the disease, myself, and the process. I chose to listen and read, talk and write, understand and question. All of these opportunities that were laid at my feet were unraveled, dissected, analyzed, felt, integrated, let go, or, in some way, dealt with. I've taken these priceless nuggets of wisdom that I hadn't previously known and written thoughtfully about each one as they unfolded.

Though the treatments and my ability to let go of the disease were extremely important, I knew that I was at a crucial turning point in my mental and spiritual evolution. While I took on the daily challenges of scheduling and keeping appointments (sometimes ten or more in a week) and staying healthy enough to continue receiving chemotherapy treatments, I also took on the challenge of figuring out what I was to learn from this major life event. By doing so, I would be able to be free of the fear of the disease and, therefore, deal with cancer with grace, humor, and positivity.

About the Book

My blog was the springboard for the book you're now holding. I want to share with you the things I learned during the years I went through cancer treatment, and my blog posts provide the window into that world in real-time. In retrospect, it's ironic to me that I chose the name *Blog about My Boobs* because so very little of this experience actually turned out to be *about* my boobs. But in the beginning, I didn't know that.

My blog, that began as a way to inform and update my friends and family, bloomed into my lifeline. Each post is akin to snapping a picture of something that could vanish in the blink of an eye. I passionately wanted to capture everything about my experience with cancer in those moments before they were over—the power, the realness, the significance. Once each moment was released onto the page embracing my emotions and employing my expressions, I clicked the button, and it was saved forever. Now, any time I look back on a post, I can remember exactly what I felt in that instant. I remember what was so frustrating or difficult or helpful or inspiring. In writing my blog, I was at once talking to everyone and no one. It was both public and private. It was simultaneously my present and my memory.

I am grateful that I adopted the path of writing. It granted me the opportunity to process and illuminate, in the moment, a wealth of experiences and information which awakened my healing. And now, it provides me with a living diary—a sort of memory surrogate during the times of stress, brain fog, and fatigue that I navigated during those years.

This book is not intended to be a motivational memoir or a "how-to" of cancer care. I offer my experiences with complementary therapies such as acupuncture, herbs, guided imagery, and yoga. And I will detail my understanding of chemotherapy, mastectomy, radiation, and reconstruction. You may not choose to read straight through but rather find the posts that speak to you in an order that flows with your experience, treatment plan, or mental state. This book could serve as a resource for families and caregivers to get a glimpse of what their loved ones who are dealing with cancer could be going through.

Because every person's familiarity with cancer, treatments, surgeries, and recovery is different, I want to be careful in saying that all of what I have written is based *solely* on my individual life story. I am not a doctor; I have no secret cure. I won't fearmonger or plant thought viruses in the minds of people who are dealing with cancer. By sharing my reality and the knowledge I gained, I hope others can learn how to release themselves from living life according to expected outcomes and to learn that accepting things for what they honestly are is true freedom.

And so, we begin.

"Your body's ability to heal is greater than anyone has permitted you to believe."

—Anonymous

Chapter One

Diagnosis and Planning

"Why I'm Starting a Blog"
December 7, 2014

I won't say that I was ready to hear the news, but it wasn't terribly shocking. I could see it on the faces and hear it in the meta-message of the technicians and the radiologist long before the diagnosis was positive for malignancy. I've known since Halloween that something wasn't right. I was finally delivered the news last Wednesday, December 3, that I have cancer in my left breast and in a lymph node under my left arm (that we know about so far).

Since then, I've been busy. I've been researching doctors and treatment centers. I've been going to appointments and consultations. I've been telling my friends and family. And I've been thinking, considering, weighing. So, if you've called me and I haven't called you back, please know that I want to. And I *so* appreciate your offers of help and encouragement. That's why I've set up a blog. I want each and every one of you to know what's going on—and I can't make enough time in the day to do that individually. I hope you will comment and ask me questions. I hope you'll share your stories and insight.

What I know right now is that I have invasive ductal carcinoma. The mass is big(ish) at five centimeters. Yes, I've been getting mammograms since I was about thirty. Yes, I have a family history—my mom had breast cancer. And yes, I do self-exams. My mammogram was due this year [2014], and I talked to my doctor about it at my annual physical in October. She felt the same lump during my clinical breast exam. I wasn't sure if it was anything different from the fibrous cysts I've felt in the past, but this one hurt and we both thought it wasn't normal. We scheduled a thermogram. In the following weeks, the pain and swelling worsened. Once the thermogram showed areas of concern, I went on to have an ultrasound. Then a mammogram. Then a biopsy. Which has led me here.

After the biopsy, I had an MRI with contrast dye and a chest X-ray. I've also had my blood drawn for genetic testing. Because I'm under forty-five, that was recommended. Most people who get breast cancer are a little older. I still need a PET scan and am waiting for my full pathology report. I've met with one really great breast surgeon. I am scheduled to meet with two more doctors on Tuesday. After that, I hope to have chosen my team and know my treatment plan. There's a lot to do when first diagnosed.

I've been reading almost nonstop because I want to contribute to my recovery as much as possible. I'm not reading about statistics and outcomes. I am living in the present. That means I'm reading about foods I can eat every day that will aid in my healing. I'm reading about dealing with stress and negative emotions. I'm also exploring adjunct therapies that are less traditional in typical Western medicine. I'm still practicing yoga and meditation and am investigating some other possibilities. I'm also going to see a therapist next week.

My husband, Michael, has been going with me to my appointments and helped me tell the kids last week. We know that what lies ahead will be challenging. But I know where I'm lucky. I'm lucky that I have friends and family who are willing to help me through this to a complete recovery. I'm lucky that my cancer is in an organ that can be removed. And I'm lucky that it hurt. Without the pain, I might not have known for some time.

I'll know a lot more after Tuesday. I'll fill you in then.

"Consultation Marathon"
December 9, 2014

Today I met with a team of doctors at [a university hospital] and a breast surgeon at [a large network medical center]. I have a tremendous amount of information, and I'm wiped out from an entire day of appointments—literally eight a.m. to five p.m.—followed by grocery shopping and dinner prep.

I haven't decided on a course of treatment yet. There's still so much to consider. But I'm weighing my options and asking for advice from some people I trust who deal with this stuff every day. So, this post is going to be short and sweet. I am still awaiting some more pathology results. I really liked some of the doctors and nurses I met with. I think I've found some good people and am working on assembling my Breast Cancer Dream Team.

More to come in the following days.

"A Serious Case of Infobesity"
December 11, 2014

Over the last few days, I've felt pretty overwhelmed by the information overload I've been given. In seven days, I went from being handed a diagnosis to having met with six doctors, a genetic counselor, a clinical study coordinator, and two nurse navigators, plus having three additional diagnostic/staging tests. Also in that time, I had to tell my kids and all my friends and family. So, I've been tired. I feel well physically, but just drained. My throat hurts from talking too much. That's why I don't always pick up my phone. I'm sorry. I'm making a list of calls to return.

All the doctors say, "I know this is a lot of information to throw at you at once," and then they throw more. I'm an educated woman with the capacity to digest information and grasp details. Maybe, in this case, it's a bad thing. I've always said that having a good memory is a blessing and a curse.

I've been swimming in this sea of "choices." Over and over, I hear, "That's an option" and "This is available to you," but medical professionals will not say what path I "should" take. It's up to me to boil it all down and rule out what I can. Then decide what's best for me. Most of the time, you can wing it with decisions. Chocolate cake? Lemon cake? Both, please! But these decisions are literally life and death. It's no piece of cake.

All three hospitals/doctors I've met with concur that chemotherapy, mastectomy, and radiation are all necessary for me. The surgeon I really loved suggested surgery first then chemo and radiation. The other two said chemo first. The idea behind doing chemo first is that the chemo will give the medical oncologist information about how the tumor reacts, how quickly, and how completely. If you remove the tumor first, you get no such information. A downside is that during chemo, the lymph nodes turn into mush so there's a less clean resection. And it's in two lymph nodes that they know of so far. There are trade-offs, but not in survival. A study was published in 1997 that showed that there was no difference in survival between patients who received chemotherapy first or second, to the surprise of the medical community.

Really, there's no wrong answer. It's a matter of choosing what I feel is best for me, what makes me most comfortable. I've talked with my nephew Aaron, (for those who don't know, he's a pathologist). He is hands-down the smartest guy I know. Simply put, he's clinically brilliant in addition to being caring and enlightened. We've discussed all the scenarios, including my need to surround myself with the right people, feeling positive vibes from my team of healers, and how important the psyche is in healing. I need that. If I feel that I have a buy-in from my team, and that they care about me as a person and don't view me as another cancer case that needs their attention, I will do better. I got those vibes from the surgical oncologist I met with last.

She said that she feels I'm very curable. She feels that she can give me a great surgical result, and she put me in touch with a plastic surgeon who she believes can give me a fantastic cosmetic result. For me, I'm most interested in curing my cancer. I plan to survive and thrive. And part of what will make me happiest in that intention is to look as much like myself as possible.

The plan is this: I'm having a PET scan next week as my last test in the staging process. Then I'm meeting with another medical oncologist next Friday. He works at [a large network medical center] alongside the surgical oncologist I'm in love with. Then two days later, I'm meeting with a plastic surgeon at [the same medical center] who is highly recommended by the surgical oncologist. The nurse navigator I'm working with believes that they will be a good fit for me. She's been a real Godsend.

I want to thank a few people for being awesome. To all the people who've texted, called, and messaged me—thank you for your concern, for taking the time to check in, and even offering help. I will take you up on that once I need it. Right now, I am fine. But there will be a time that I'll need a ride or a prescription picked up or a movie night. I'll call you.

And now, you all have infobesity too.

"A Third Eye-Opening Experience"
December 16, 2014

No one *wants* cancer. But because I have it, there are things I can learn from the experience.

One thing I've learned is that I approach cancer the way I do everything: head-on. I'm not aware of another way, so this is natural. I approach it with the serious attention it deserves without allowing it to paralyze me with fear. Right now, I'm feeling a little stifled by the process within the medical community, so I've started to branch out and seek new ways to care for myself while I plan for my treatment.

I also know that humor goes a long way. A few laughs and some lighthearted moments make me feel like the situation isn't *so* dire that we can't crack a joke.

I'm learning that I don't have to accept anyone's idea of what *will* happen to me. "You'll be sick," "You'll feel tired." Maybe. But I don't have to accept that as fact and invite it into my life. The medical community may be trying to "educate" me on what to expect, but their thought viruses can be very powerful, because we're supposed to trust and believe everything they say. Thanks to many survivors, I am aware of the solutions to the side effects of chemotherapy and ways to cope with the surgery.

I've learned that there's no time like to present to appreciate all the wonderful people in my life. Like my husband. Yesterday, he went with me to an appointment in Boulder. After, we had an amazing dinner on Pearl Street, strolled the walking mall for a bit, and then shopped at the Twenty-Ninth Street Mall. We Christmas shopped and had a normal day. It was sunny when we started out. There was snow on the Flatirons. It was beautiful—in every way.

I've learned that listening to my gut is the only way I know how to make a decision. It's always been that way for me, and it rarely steers me wrong. I have strong intuition. I try to keep my third-eye chakra open (a.k.a. the yogic "eye of insight"), allowing myself to be aware and accepting of the wisdom and intuition present when I trust my Self, allowing me to heal in body, mind, and spirit.

"A Negative Is a Positive"
December 17, 2014

I don't have a lot of news, but I do have one piece of extraordinarily good news. I do not have any BRCA gene mutations! Some of you might know what this means. For the rest of the people, like me, the following explanation is what I've been able to glean from a variety of online sources and boil it down to, for me, the most important points. Please simply join me in a collective sigh of relief. One, two, three . . . sigh!

BRCA1 and BRCA2 are human genes that, when specific inherited mutations are present, increase the risk of breast and ovarian cancers. Mutations of these genes can be linked to certain breast cancers that are more aggressive and harder to treat than other types.

"Thrive"
December 18, 2014

Yesterday, I had an appointment with a radiation oncologist who I really liked and will be added to my team of caregivers. In our conversation, he reminded me that the most important goal in my treatment is survival. Well . . . duh. I say that with respect, actually, because of course it is, and I'm glad that's his primary goal! However, I feel like when I ask about anything functional or cosmetic, I am reminded that their first priority is my survival. I have really only one response to that: "If I weren't planning on 'surviving' then why would I care if I end up with permanently discolored skin from radiation?" I happen to be *so* positive about my prognosis that I'm asking questions about what the reconstruction will look like in twenty, thirty years. I think it's dangerous to get caught in "survival" mode. That's what you do when you're hanging from a cliff and hungry alligators below are jumping at your heels. That's not me. I will thrive.

That said, of course I will treat this disease very aggressively, utilizing all the modalities at my disposal until I am cured. But I'm not just a body. It's very important in the course of curing the cancer that I honor the other parts of my Self and not think of any aspect as "less important."

I understand that hair grows back, and I'll have reconstructed breasts, but it won't be the same hair or the same breasts that I have now. And it's important for me to mourn the loss of these things—and others that I haven't even gotten around to thinking of yet. This is a trauma for the body as well as the mind and spirit.

I feel that it's dangerous to view breast cancer as "routine." When do we make the most mistakes? When we're doing something absentmindedly. So, I certainly don't want my doctors asleep at the wheel. But theirs is only one piece of the healing. It's key for me to remember that my oncologists' job is to treat cancer. And it's up to me to seek ways of treating my mind and spirit. I do feel that the surgical oncologist and the radiation oncologist I've chosen so far are on board with that. They're positive and open-minded people who have expressed recognition that I'm a whole person sitting across the desk from them.

Later today, I'm going to see my primary care physician. Following are the first two paragraphs of his website to give you an idea of the kind of doctor he is and how I hope he can help me.

> *"We believe that there is more than one path that leads to good health. In fact, you may need multiple paths to get where you want to be: enjoying a high quality of life with the energy and motivation to fully participate in your daily experiences.*
>
> *"Our unique approach features the best of what both Western and Eastern medicines have to offer. Relying on sophisticated laboratory testing, your care will be guided by a board-certified MD with over thirty-two years in private practice. From there, Japanese acupuncture, Chinese herbal therapies, powerful nutritional supplements, and homeopathic remedies may be part of your individualized treatment. The ideal combination for each patient is different."*

His name is Butch Levy.

Additionally, the radiation oncology nurse said that they will write me a prescription for physical therapy for me to regain my strength, my flexibility, and my posture. She said, "If you're willing to go, we will write it!" Sounds like many patients don't take advantage of that. Crazy talk! We also discussed some other "alternative prescriptions" (i.e., CBD) they will write for me should I find the need for help with nausea, appetite enhancement, and the overall ability to chill. Yes, all forms of CBD are legal here in Colorado, but it's way less expensive to purchase it from a medical dispensary, in addition to better regulation.

I've mentioned her before and I will again now: My therapist, Sally, will be my biggest advocate and resource for mental and spiritual health, support, and guidance in this process. I meditate. I laugh. I talk about how I feel. I release negative emotions. I prepare my body and mind for the upcoming surgery. I read. I watch

Jon Stewart. And I mourn the loss of *The Colbert Report*. I've still got my Fallon, but still . . .

Thank you to everyone who is sending positive, healing vibes my way. It takes a village.

"Good News"
December 19, 2014

So much good news today, I don't know where to begin. I guess I'll just dive right in—my PET scan is clear! The PET scan is the test that looks at my whole body to see if the cancer has spread anywhere else. And the answer is . . . no! The cancer is contained in the left breast and the left axillary lymph nodes that we already knew about. And the rest of my body is clear—lungs, liver, bones—everywhere—are all clear!

The other good news is that I met with the medical oncologist this morning—literally starting before dawn—for four hours! To say he was thorough is an understatement. It was great to feel so understood and listened to. We decided that I will start chemotherapy and immunotherapy next Friday, December 26. I will have six treatments of chemotherapy, once every twenty-one days on a Thursday. Each time, the following morning, I will get an injection to help prevent infections during the course of the chemotherapy treatment. The immunotherapy drugs will continue at the same frequency for a year. Being on this schedule puts my surgery in early May.

I will get a port placed in my right arm on Tuesday, December 23, for the treatments. The oncologist said that there is usually very little nausea with the medication I will be given. There may be some fatigue associated with these drugs, but the best way to combat the fatigue is exercise. *Now* they're speaking my language. He said that thirty minutes of exercise, seven days a week is the key. He was crystal clear on that point: "Not six, not five—seven." Consider it done. For my local friends, I'd love to have some walking and yoga partners.

And lastly—I got my hair cut. I wanted to have my hair short in preparation for when it falls out. The oncologist said it starts to fall out around two to two and a half weeks after the first treatment. I had to go to a new hair stylist because my regular one couldn't fit me in for quite a while. She was *great*. When I was done and tried to pay, she said it was on the house because she knew that I was getting ready to start chemo. It was so incredibly nice of her (I just met her an hour before) that I got flustered and rushed out without even tipping her. Don't worry, I made my daughter go back in to give her the money because I didn't want to cry in public a second time.

Long day. Off to bed. I think I'll sleep well.

"My Dream Team"
December 24, 2014

It's been twenty-one days since I was diagnosed with breast cancer. And it took me nearly all that time to find the doctors that I trust to treat me and my condition. It wasn't easy. Now I have three oncologists, an integrative-medicine doctor, and a reconstructive surgeon that I am counting on to see me through this. They are:

- **Medical oncologist**—He'll be the one to oversee the administration of my chemo- and immunotherapy, which will take place between now and about next Christmas. He's the most thorough doctor I've ever met. And hands-down gives the best breast exam. Take my word on this. I've had a lot.
- **Surgical oncologist**—She will be the one to perform my bilateral mastectomy in May. She's the most compassionate surgeon I've ever met. Her technical skill along with her personal engagement sold me on creating my team at [this medical center.]
- **Radiation oncologist**—He will be the one to oversee the administration of my radiation therapy in the June timeframe. Between him and his nurse, I was carefully and completely explained the process, the benefits and the risks of radiation. I'm much less worried about that step now and have faith in his abilities.

- **Dr. Butch Levy, integrative-medicine doctor**—He will be the one to provide me with supplements, techniques, and homeopathy to make all of the cancer treatments more tolerable. He has extensive experience working with people who have cancer and recognizes the necessity of Western therapies and how Eastern therapies can complement them. He has been the main doctor at my PCP practice. He's had my trust for years. He was the first doctor to listen to me about my son's problems with gluten and diagnosed him with celiac disease. He has already had a conversation with my medical oncologist to make sure they're on the same page.

- **Reconstructive surgeon**—He will be the one to perform my breast reconstruction beginning in May, at the time of the mastectomy, and ending around spring of 2016, depending on how far I decide to take the process of reconstruction. He's the only doctor I've met so far who matches my "earthy" sense of humor. It's not for everyone, but it resonated with me. I've seen his "before and after" photos and I trust him to do everything he can for me to be happy to have an "after" photo taken.

I start chemo in about forty-eight hours, finally. I'm very ready to begin the healing. I've had numerous diagnostic tests in these last three weeks which now provide the full picture of what we're dealing with.

It goes like this: I have invasive ductal carcinoma in my left breast that is locally advanced. I have a mass approximately five centimeters, which was biopsied, in addition to two satellite lesions, calcifications, and some areas which appear to be ductal carcinoma in situ (DCIS). DCIS is non-invasive cancer that exists only in the milk duct and hasn't invaded surrounding tissue. It's not life-threatening in itself but does increase the risk of developing invasive cancer.

I also have one lymph node that was biopsied and showed pathological evidence of disease. Another node looks involved from the MRI. The PET scan showed no dissemination of cancer to any other part of my body. The genetic testing showed that I have no genetic mutations. All of this I continue to celebrate daily.

The biomarkers of the cancer I have are ER/PR negative, HER2 positive. ER/PR stands for estrogen receptor/progesterone receptor. For people whose status is positive, it means that the cancer grows in response to one or both of these hormones. Mine does not. The HER2 part is a description of a kind of cancer that makes too much of a protein called HER2/neu. My status has been equivocal at every level of testing and repeated testing. I do, however, show some cancer cells which express this characteristic. Therefore, I will be treated with immunotherapy medications for a year just like chemotherapy, except they're not associated with as many side effects and increase my cure rate by a lot.

That's all about the "kind" of breast cancer I have. There's also "grade" and "stage." My grade is a 2. Basically, there are three grades: 1, 2, and 3. What the pathologists look at to determine the grade is how like or unlike the nuclei of cancer cells are compared to normal nuclei. Grade 1 means that it looks close-ish to a normal nucleus. Grade 3 means that varies significantly from a normal nucleus. Grade 2 is in between. My Medical Oncologist tells me that, typically, women my age tend to have the highest grade which tends to be more aggressive. I celebrate my Grade 2 status daily.

Lastly, stage: I have stage III. Having cancer at all makes it stage I. Involvement of lymph nodes makes it stage II. The size of my tumor makes it stage III.

I'm learning a lot about cancer in this process—specifically that not all cancer cells are the same. Meaning that even within the tumor I have, cells vary and concentrations vary. I also learned that I will have more pathologic studies done along the way to determine if there's any change in my biomarkers.

I really don't like characterizing something as "good" or "bad." It just *is*. It's what I'm dealing with. It's what my doctors are trained to deal with. My cancer is as individual as I am. My response will be equally unique.

"What's Jim Carrey Got to Do with This?"
December 24, 2014

In Jim Carrey's graduation speech at Maharishi University of Management's class of 2014, I found true inspiration. It's twenty-six minutes that really get to the point—of life.

Two ideas resonated with me: The first is hope. We use the term a lot. But I am not a fan. I agree with Jim Carrey that it sounds more like begging than believing. I much prefer to have faith. Faith in what makes sense to me—a higher power, my doctors, myself, my family, my loved ones, my friends. That faith is much more important to me now—more than ever before. I have faith in my doctors' capabilities. I have faith that the universe presented this opportunity to me for a reason and that I'll have many more opportunities for decades to come. I have faith that I am strong enough to understand and work with my body to heal completely. I have faith that my family, my loved ones, and my friends will be there for me throughout and beyond.

Jim Carrey's speech continues on the topic of making choices out of love, not fear. Those are our only two root options. Always have been, always will be. I am reminded of two songs when I hear this: AWOL Nation's "Kill Your Heroes" and Andrew McMahon's "Cecilia and the Satellite." I continue to try to make decisions from a place of love. That's not saying that I *don't* feel fear—far from it. But sometimes you have to face the fear, deal with it, and find a way to allow love to triumph.

"My Responsible Party"
December 24, 2014

The insurance company calls him my "responsible party." The surgery center calls him my "driver." The oncologist calls him my "caregiver." My medical history lists him as my "emergency contact." My HIPAA forms designate him as the "other" person who can receive medical information about me.

And he is all of these things. But to me, he's my husband,

Michael, and he's simply "there." I mean this in the best way possible. He's there to "hold this," "fix this," "tie this stupid gown," "open this damn jar."

He's there for me to vent about the surgery center giving him my discharge papers instead of me and about the lab that continues to overlook me and give my results directly to doctors that I'm not even working with. He's there when I worry that my arm and finger are a little numb after my port placement (totally normal and now completely resolved). He's there when I have to make really tough decisions about the order of my treatments. He's there when I say I want another tamale. He's there when I'm "hangry"—it's happened a lot lately because of all the fasting for tests and appointments. He's there when I laugh way too loud at seventh-grade jokes. He's there to walk with me, between appointments, around the hospital campus when it drops twenty degrees and begins to snow even though he forgot his gloves in the car and has nothing to cover his ears just so I can comply with my oncologist's instructions to get some kind of activity for thirty minutes a day.

When I ask him about decisions I'm trying to make, he gives me his advice. And says that he trusts me to make the decisions that are right for me and in the end, he just cares that his wife is here.

So, honey, that's what I'm trying to do—make sure I'm "there" for you.

"More than Words"
December 24, 2014

One thing I've discovered in this process is that I don't like being termed a "cancer patient" or a "chemo patient." Instead, I'm a person who is dealing with cancer. I'm a person who has chosen to receive chemotherapy treatment. I suppose that's why I'm not particularly a fan of pink-ribbon wear. I don't fault people who are. I just believe that it's limiting to assume that every person who deals with breast cancer will handle it the same. To me, I'm not a diagnosis. So it's odd to me to receive a gift that has a pink ribbon on it. Does that really represent who I am? Not at all.

I have chosen to not let cancer define me. I'm a giant list of all sorts of things before I had cancer and have faith that I will be many more after.

Treatment Schedule

As I can best calculate, my dates for chemotherapy treatment will be: December 26, January 15, February 5, February 26, March 19, and April 9. My immunotherapy treatments will continue on this three-week basis for another eight months, finishing in December of 2015.

My surgery will take place three weeks after chemotherapy ends. And radiation therapy will start six to eight weeks after chemotherapy treatment ends.

There are too many unknowns about reconstruction to speculate but I think that the first phase will take place at the time of the mastectomy.

"Nothing ever goes away until it has taught us what we need to know."

—Pema Chödrön

Chapter Two

Chemotherapy, Round 1

"Treatment Is Underway"
December 27, 2014

Y esterday, December 26, I had my first treatment with chemotherapy and immunotherapy. It was a long day, but all things considered, not bad. I checked in at 10:30 a.m. and left at 6:00 p.m. I was given a mix of premedications which included long-acting anti-nausea medication and a steroid to help alleviate any potential allergic reactions. Then I was given the immunotherapy medications first, which lasted two and a half hours. Then two chemotherapy drugs which lasted two hours. Luckily, I had no adverse reactions, and it all went well. I had a nurse that was good and attentive. I had warm blankets at my disposal. I had a hot-water dispenser available as well.

I passed the time by playing my favorite word game with Michael. I think that "technically" he beat me, but I'm still arguing for style points. My words were more obscure and less formulaic. He claims it's only about the points. Whatever. I think that "ribosome" and "crimson" deserve more points than "threaten" and "threatens." But that's just me.

I also cracked open my *Thug Kitchen* cookbook which looks

yummy and is entertaining at the same time. My hubby got us lunches from the hospital (Greek salad for me and some fruit I stashed in my backpack). I'm still surprised by the lack of attention given to diet in the hospital. The fridge in the infusion room was stocked with sodas and fruit juice and there's a basket of junk food snacks. Even the nurse said, "We don't have anything healthy, so if you want that, you're welcome to bring your own." Done.

I've decided that I really, really need a pair of noise-canceling headphones. The infusion room is generally open with a nurses' desk and a small kitchen area. I heard so many conversations of other patients that I really could have done without ever hearing. Ever.

Overall, I was warm, fed, entertained, comfortable, and cared for. Considering that I have no choice but to do this five more times, it was not as bad as I feared.

Today, I had to go to the outpatient clinic to get an injection which stimulates the bone marrow to produce more white blood cells and reduces my overall risk of infection.

I still feel well. I did pick up a cold and that's the only thing that's annoying me—a heavy head and runny nose. I was told the steroid could wire me up last night, so they gave me an anti-anxiety medication to help me sleep. Help it did! I was out and slept through the night. I was still up before my alarm went off, but what else is new?

"Well, Yesterday Sucked"
December 29, 2014

I have a cold at the same time as I'm dealing with chemo, so I couldn't tell what was what. But overall, I felt bad: tired, diarrhea, nausea, and general shittiness. Today, I feel better. I went to see Butch and he gave me a six-herb blend to help with the digestion, and tomorrow I start acupuncture with him. I'm very excited for that. The American medical insurance system is very messed up. My acupuncture is not covered. Luckily, it's only seventy-five dollars a visit, but still . . .

Good news on the financial side of things: we talked to the billing/insurance person at the oncologist's office and she has been very proactive in verifying my benefits and taking it on herself to apply for some pharmaceutical grants offered for three of the medicines I'm taking. Basically, each of my treatments will cost tens of thousands of dollars. My insurance covers 80 percent and then these pharmaceutical grants will pay a bunch so that my remaining balance is only $477. The news gets better—that's only for the first one, till I meet my deductible and my annual out-of-pocket, which will happen after one and a half treatments. After that, I'll be covered at 100 percent. So, I'll pay about $750 total for chemotherapy and immunotherapy.

She said, "You have excellent insurance." Hell yeah! I can't imagine having financial hardship on top of all of this! Like Forrest Gump said, "One less thing."

I'm very excited to have acupuncture tomorrow. I really believe it will help.

"What a Difference a Butch Makes"
January 2, 2015

I'm glad I felt well today. This past week has been a roller coaster. Here's the deal: chemo kills all of your fast-growing cells—including the cancer—but also hair, nails, stomach lining, etc. For me, it wrecked my intestines. Just wiped it all out. Which isn't good for doing things like eating and digesting food, which are kind of important. The thing is, in the Western medical community, the oncologist just wants you to stop the diarrhea. Now. Do not pass go. Do not collect $200. Just take anti-diarrhea medicine, ad nauseam (literally). I was directed to take a double dose the first time, then a single dose every two hours for twelve hours, till nighttime, then double doses every four hours, continuing until it stops for twenty-four hours. Well, it works like a charm! If you don't care about feeling like crap.

The nausea that ensued, coupled with the rumbling and distended abdomen, were enough to lay me up all day—all week! The problem is that the medicine just stops the symptom, but it doesn't fix the problem. The problem will return when the medicine is discontinued. I was a wreck about mid-week. I had a BP of 78/58, was dehydrated, and I couldn't think of a single food that I wanted to attempt.

Enter Butch. Remember him? He's my PCP with mad Eastern medicine skills. He's got me on the road to recovery. With the help of acupuncture, prebiotics, probiotics, high-dose, digestion-friendly herbs, nutrition advice, and recipes, we recolonized my lower intestines! I am eating three meals a day and feeling well enough to do the exercise bike for an hour and go shopping.

Tomorrow morning, I go back to see Butch for more acupuncture and an adjustment of my herb dose. I'm feeling much more confident that we have the problem managed, and I will be able to get my next treatment later this month.

I went out of the house today for the first time in a week (for something other than a doctor's appointment.) It may not have been glamorous, but it felt like an extravaganza.

I got brand-new, clean, fresh, unspoiled 2015 calendars. I love, love, love new calendars! They're so full of possibilities. And I bought a particularly pretty one this time. No waterfalls and kittens, just a pretty design in a calming color with lots and lots of blank pages. And a desk pad. Yes, I still use a desk pad. I also got a new vanity seat for my bathroom.

My sister Kerrianne went home on Friday after being here for almost two weeks. It wasn't the usual kind of Christmas trip she spends here, but it was great for me to have her here to help. She cooked, cleaned, drove my butt around, took my daughter, Aspen, shopping and for lunch and nails, played Hangman with my son, Zach, and delighted us with her New Year's dance. Thank you for everything!

"My Hair"
January 6, 2015

My oncologist says that by next fall, my hair will be grown back enough that I'll need "styling." That made me chuckle when he said it for some reason.

This seems like a trivial thing, but it's something we all think about when we know someone is going through chemotherapy:

"Will she lose her hair?" The answer for me is yes. I haven't yet. I'm told my scalp will start to tingle and then the hair will fall out—not all at once, probably around seventeen to twenty-one days after my first treatment. Right now, I'm at eleven days. So, I still have my hair.

I've decided that I'm not going to use cold caps. They're a new product available from a few companies that enable people undergoing chemotherapy to keep their hair. I don't understand the technology entirely, but somehow the frozen temps of the caps preserve the hair follicles. The caps have to be kept frozen and you wear them for hours before, during, and after chemotherapy, switching them out to keep them cold. They are so new on the market that they're not FDA approved (eye roll), therefore insurance companies won't cover them. And they're pricey—around $3,000. To me, it's not that important. It'd be different if my hair never grew back. But it will.

I'm also not going to get a wig. That is something my insurance would cover, but I don't want one. I'm not interested in trying to look like I have hair. I will cover my head with scarves, bandanas, and hats, but mostly because it's the middle of winter and I already get so cold. My hair is like a head and neck blanket! I will miss it for that reason, and I will cover my head for that reason. But I'm not all that concerned about being bald. I have wondered more than once what I'd look like bald. I'm about to find out.

There's a chance that I'll lose my eyebrows and eyelashes. Not everyone does. And I understand that if a person does, it's usually toward the end of treatment. That freaks me out a little more than the hair on my head. I'm not sure why, but somehow changing the look of my eyes changes the look of "me" more than what's on top of my head. Again, the brows and lashes will grow back if they do fall out. So, not the end of the world.

"Gute Nachrichten"
January 11, 2015

That means "good news" in German.

Since I last posted, I went for my post-surgical follow-up with the surgeon who implanted my port. She took out the stitches, removed the adhesive bandages, and gave me clearance to drive again. Because the port is in my right arm, my range of motion was too limited to drive safely. But I'm nearly back to 100 percent. In fact, the other night I woke up with my arm above my head. True story.

I also got clearance to go back to yoga. I'm so happy for that. She said I should not do weight-bearing poses on that arm yet but I should stretch it gently as much as possible to keep scar tissue from forming. She said that by February, I could probably lift more than eight pounds and start to bear weight on my right arm in yoga. I am geared up to get back into it. I've still been doing my exercise bike every day for thirty to sixty minutes. It's pretty boring, but considering how cold it's been and how messy the sidewalks, roads, and trails are, it's a good substitute. I keep it right next to my bed. When I roll out in the morning, I do the bike. Then I move on with my day.

And now that I can drive again, I figured it was time for a new car. (Well, new to me and . . . that's not the *only* reason.) I got it yesterday. I love it. I've had my eye on this car for about six months. I went to look at a few and decided on mine. It's white with a black leather interior, heated seats, sunroof, satellite radio, AWD, a 3.5L V6 engine, and a five-speed automatic transmission. It's zippy and cute. Just perfect.

This last part isn't necessarily good news, but it's long-anticipated. My hair started falling out yesterday. I ran my hand through it and pulled out a large cluster. Luckily, I have a ton of hair. Despite losing a bunch of hair in the shower and during blow-drying it today, it looks the same. I've been waffling on whether or not to go back to the salon and have it shaved, but I'm not ready yet. My hair still looks too good to do that to it. So, I'll wait until I feel like I need to. I've been trying out my scarves and hats to decide what I'll wear, and I think they look pretty cute. But I'm in no rush.

Tomorrow I will see Butch again for acupuncture and to talk about my preventive care going into Thursday's treatment (chemo, round 2). I'm looking forward to seeing my oncologist and having him take a measurement of the shrinkage of the tumor. With the tumor being in my breast I can see and feel the tumor and can tell it's smaller. I'm able to fit into both sides of my bra again, and the pain has been gone for a couple weeks. I was told that I'd be able to notice the shrinkage, and I can.

"Fish and Rice and Vegetables"
January 12, 2015

That's what I've been eating. But sometimes I get wacky and mix it up. I'll have vegetables and fish and rice. Seriously though, I know they're very good for me, and normally I really like all of these things, but I've been eating them three times a day. Sometimes it's salmon, others it's cod or halibut. They're incredibly calming, nourishing, and easily digested, but I'm ready for some meat.

I saw Butch this morning and he said I could try to eat some meat. Particularly if it's slow-cooked and I have a few ounces at a time. He said my digestive energy is good. He gave me some vegan protein shakes to drink and started me on some herbs in preparation for my second round of infusions on Thursday. He also wants me to come back on Thursday right after my infusions for another acupuncture session to calm things down right away.

I've lost a little bit of weight. Not a ton, but enough that Butch wants me to start eating more nut butters and stir-fry my vegetables in olive oil for some plant-based fats. I'm still eating the stewed apple recipe he gave me and am able to eat an uncooked banana. But, man, I could definitely go for a slow-cooked pot roast with carrots. Perhaps tomorrow. It's a little late to start that now.

Butch said that he's not going to be too strict with my diet during this process, it's all about what I will tolerate and keeping my weight, blood pressure, and energy up. With one exception, "No crap." I assured him that crap is not normally part of my diet so that is not a problem.

"New Car, New Food, New Me!"
January 12, 2015

Well, maybe not a new me, but it sure feels that way! Between my dinner and a wonderful yoga class, I'm feeling great.

My dinner wasn't a dramatic departure from the fish, rice, and veggies routine, but OMG did it taste good! It was brown-rice pasta with zucchini, baby portabella mushrooms, tomatoes, and fresh oregano sauteed in olive oil.

The yoga class went very well. There are only a few things I can't do because of the weight-bearing limitation of my right arm. But I could do 90 percent. I look forward to going back tomorrow morning.

"Round Two"
January 14, 2015

Tomorrow, I will go back for round two of chemotherapy. I am less nervous this time. I have faith that this round will be better. I have some idea of what side effects I might have, and I have a better grip on how to handle them, many thanks to Butch for that.

I have been feeling great these last few days. I'm going to yoga again in about an hour. I'll use that time to focus on the present, to help my body prepare for tomorrow, and to set an intention of positive thinking.

In yoga class when we do tree pose, we do it twice, once on each leg. Balancing on the first leg, my instructor guides us to stretch out our arms and focus on the goodness that the universe offers to us and after a moment of steadiness, we bring our hands back to center, harnessing that positive energy and folding it into our hearts. For the second leg, she guides us to outstretch our arms and focus on the goodness that we can offer out to the universe. I love that idea of giving and receiving goodness, light, and energy and, each time, bringing that intention back to your heart.

Yesterday, I tried to go to yoga. But I ended up in a mat Pilates class. It wasn't like, "Oops! I slipped and fell into Pilates." It turns out that that Tuesday session of yoga doesn't begin until January

20, and I didn't know it. So, my friend and I decided to give Pilates a shot. It was a good class from an exercise standpoint. But, boy, I missed yoga. I like the things that yoga offers that nothing else can. I like moving my body with purpose and intention. I like the breathing and the mindfulness. I sweat my butt off in yoga, but I also sweat my mind off.

When I leave yoga, I'm clear-headed. I'm energized. I'm positive. I'm grateful to be going to yoga this evening, on chemo eve. It'll be wonderful to get my mind, heart, and soul ready.

Thank you to all who have offered me well wishes, prayed for me, and kept me in their thoughts. Thank you for all the positive, healing energy coming my way. Namaste.

By the way, I made pot roast last night. I went to the grocery store and got a good cut, some red potatoes, and multicolored carrots. It was heaven. Pot roast is good for my soul.

Chapter Three

Chemotherapy, Round 2

"One-Third Done"
January 15, 2015

T hank you to everyone for all the positive thoughts, words of encouragement, and prayers for me. Today, I completed my second round of chemotherapy! It's done! In the books. Banked. Water under the bridge. Over.

The fact that it actually happened is not to be taken for granted. It was a matter of question this morning. I got there, and met with my oncologist, who definitely agreed with me that the tumor is much softer and smaller than before. He said that it's more difficult to measure now that the margins are less clearly defined, but he said, "For sure much softer and smaller." I'm very glad that he concurs with my estimation. He said that I'll have another MRI after all six treatments and before surgery to look at the tumor again to see just how well it responded to treatment.

After my good news, I went into the infusion room to get started. Pretty soon, the nurse came over and said that they were fighting with my insurance company. Evidently, my insurance company did not require a preauthorization in 2014 for the medications I'm getting, but in 2015 they now do. Therefore, about fourteen days ago, someone should have begun a new "case" for me with new dates. But because the new case was opened only yesterday, and they require two to fifteen days to approve it, it wasn't looking good.

I don't get it. Still me. Still cancer. Same damn drugs as last time. Everyone at [the medical center] was on the phone with the insurance company. So, I called too. I figured I'm my own best advocate.

Believe it or not, I was calm(ish), I didn't yell (much) and I didn't swear (at all)—I have witnesses to prove this—despite the fact that I was told twice that the second-tier representative I was speaking with was a mere "middleman" and she understood my "frustration." I said that frustration didn't begin to describe it. Eventually, I was silent while she rattled on about dates and processes and approvals. I got calm enough to say, "What can we do to make this happen today? I'm here, in the infusion room, ready to get this treatment. There is a medical reason my oncologist wants me to have it every twenty-one days. What can be done?"

I eventually hung up after being told that they expedited my case, and I could wait to hear back directly from her on whether or not it was approved. As far as the "middleman" could guess it could be today or fifteen days from today. She followed up by saying that "usually" cancer cases are approved, but she can't guarantee it. Very reassuring.

The billing consultant at the oncologist's office gave me the options of waiting, rescheduling, or signing a waiver of financial responsibility saying that if I proceed with treatment today and it's denied, then I'd be responsible for paying $49,000 for today's chemo and $11,000 for tomorrow's injection. Yes, you read that right—$60,000 total. Insane. For *one* treatment. Because I'm not in a financial position that I can comfortably write a check for that amount, I decided to wait it out.

About three hours after my infusions were to begin, the approval came through to the billing department, for which I am grateful. So, the nurses began their job of prepping my port, drawing my labs, taking my vitals, and recording my weight (which is holding pretty steady.)

After all that, it was smooth sailing. I had lunch (leftover lemongrass roasted chicken, rice pilaf, and broccoli that I made last night), read, listened to music, played board games, and enjoyed the silence with my new noise-canceling headphones. I think I discovered the main problem with the noise level in the infusion room—the majority of the folks are quite old and they don't hear well, so they talk *loud* and a lot. Apparently, modesty has left the building. I actually heard one woman tell another that her "tree-hugging" daughter-in-law cheated on her son. *Sigh.* So much wrong with that sentence. Time for the headphones! No need to hear how that story ends, or worse.

The infusions took three hours and fifteen minutes. That's about the quickest it can get for me. I'm taking premeds (anti-nausea and steroid) and then two immunotherapy drugs and two chemotherapy drugs.

I think the most maddening part of dealing with the insurance company today was that at no point did anyone want to act like a human being and stop quoting me their new procedure. People often complain about insurance companies and big corporations, and some of them are truly reprehensible. But they're *people,* and they choose to hide behind bullshit. I can't forget that. I am a *customer* of this insurance company. I really wish people at the top of these companies would stop and think for a minute about how things are handled. Don't get me wrong, I understand the importance of having procedures in place and the necessity of following them, but telling me that I could have to wait up to fifteen days for the review board to review my case? Unacceptable. I was there for chemotherapy, not approval from the HOA on my new house paint. There is a medical reason that chemotherapy medications are given at prescribed intervals for a defined number of times in the same order by a medical oncologist.

By the way, the "middleman" who promised me that as soon as the review board reviewed my case she'd call me back directly on the cell phone number I relayed to her? She never called.

"Pura Vida"
January 15, 2015

I *love* vegetables. A lot. I love them in salads, soups, casseroles, on sandwiches, in stir fry, on pizza, raw, cooked, plain, and smothered. I haven't yet tried a vegetable that I don't like. With one important exception—lima beans. I hate them. I still pick them out.

But this girl cannot live on vegetables alone. I don't eat a lot of meat, but I feel physically better when I do. I've tried being a vegetarian. What gets me is the smell and thought of a really good, high-quality, well-cooked burger. Yep. A big warm bun and a huge hunk of meat. In paradise or not. I'll eat it here or there. I crave it. Not fast-food "meat," but pasture-raised, grass-fed, humanely raised beef or bison. I consider myself an ethical omnivore.

It's not just burgers. I love chicken schnitzel, German wurst, bison short ribs, roasted duck, slow-roasted pulled pork, pot roast, bacon, and ham. These last two aren't the healthiest choices, I know. But I choose naturally raised pork, uncured, no nitrates or nitrites added, and then I make a BKT (bacon, kale, and tomato) and eat it on my deck.

Last summer when I was in Costa Rica, I ordered a burger at a café. Everything there is fresh. Those chickens out back? Tomorrow's fajitas. Those bananas in the wheelbarrow this morning? Tonight's dessert. So, I felt comfortable ordering a burger. The Costa Ricans live by the phrase *"pura vida."* Directly translated, it means "pure life." It's about a simple, laid-back, kind, considerate way to live gratefully. The Costa Ricans seem to have an understanding of living that has escaped much of American culture.

Anyway, back to my burger. When it came, what was on it but a slice of ham! I figured they took the American word "hamburger" literally. I thought they were geniuses and savored every last bite.

The concept of food is something that changes when undergoing chemo. At least it has for me. Despite everything tasting like metal and having a constantly upset stomach, eating remains a requirement. I am eating several small meals a day, and my weight is holding steady. I guess I didn't realize how much I enjoy cooking and eating until now. I miss it. Please bear with me while I dream of my cheeseburger in paradise. Once I'm allowed to leave the country again, I'm definitely going back to Puerto Viejo, Costa Rica, for a second amazing *ham*burger. And I might just stay for the pura vida.

"General Lack of Focus, Reporting for Duty"
January 25, 2015

I haven't posted for a while. So, there's likely to be a general lack of focus here. I'll try my best to make sense of all my random ideas.

Butch—My Doctor

There's a good reason that I haven't posted for a while. I haven't felt well. In fact, I have felt like shit. I had my treatment eleven days ago, and I'm finally feeling mostly good again. This past Monday (five days after treatment), I walked into Butch's office and he asked me how I felt.

I said, "Like shit."

He said, "Well, you look like you feel like shit. Let's see what we can do about that."

I love Butch. He's a no-bullshit kind of guy. But he's not going to mope around in the bad feelings. He's going to help me feel better.

During one conversation with Butch about something my oncologist had recommended, Butch said he disagreed with the recommendation. He said that throwing another pill at the problem isn't always the answer. Then he said, "He's just your oncologist. *I'm* your doctor." I wonder if it's too late for Butch to adopt me?

I'll see him again on Monday.

Welp, I Lied

I didn't lie on purpose. But still. I said I wasn't going to get a wig for a couple of reasons. First, I didn't think I'd mind being bald. Turns out, that is not true. I hate being bald, and I got a wig. I had been wearing caps and scarves, and they were cute but all so bulky and difficult to keep in place and match with my clothes. And still, decidedly, not hair.

I was a little hesitant to start this process. My oncologist wrote my prescription for my wig calling it a "cranial prosthesis." I have to congratulate the medical community for taking a simple word and turning it into a complicated, easily misunderstood phrase.

Second, I thought that a wig would look like, well, a wig.

Third, I didn't know where to go.

Once I was ready, I started the process by asking the nurse at my oncologist's office where to turn. She directed me to a local shop dedicated to wigs and hair styling. The owner is awesome. She's a breast cancer survivor who also raises money for Hana's Hope for kids with cancer who can't afford wigs. Then there was a whole bunch of insurance stuff that happened that I won't get deep into. Short story: I had to apply for a network gap extension because there are no approved providers within thirty miles of my zip code. I rolled my eyes every time I had to say "cranial prosthesis" to the insurance company over the phone. Yadda, yadda, yadda—two to fifteen days later, my insurance will cover 80 percent of my wig.

Once I got to the shop, they were great! They were helpful, looked at recent pictures of my hair, chose some wigs for me to try, showed me how to put them on, and within less than an hour, I'd chosen a wig and was walking out with it on.

I chose one with synthetic hair. I thought I wanted natural hair, but get a load of this: you have to *style* a natural hair wig. Seriously. Blow dry, curl, straighten, whatever you'd do to your own hair, you have to do to the wig. They call it the "benefit" of a natural hair wig because you can make it look however you want. These days, I'm looking for low maintenance. Plus, these natural hair wigs aren't *your* hair; it's someone else's and it doesn't always behave the same as your own, so I would have to learn how to do someone else's hair (this kind of freaked me out). Also, real hair is heavy. In order to make a wig of natural hair look nice and full, they have to use *a lot* of hair.

That's why I went with synthetic hair. My wig is 100 percent hand-tied instead of machine-woven, so that makes it very light. It looks almost exactly like my hair did prior to losing it. And the stylist was able to cut the side bangs for me so they fall nicely over my cheek. I couldn't be happier.

The upkeep is minimal. At night, I put it on my wig rack and give it a quick brush. In the morning, after my shower, I put on the liner (looks like a nylon beanie) and slip on the wig. It looks great. And I say to my hubby, "Instant wife!" I should shampoo it every four to eight weeks depending on how much I wear it and how much I sweat. That's it.

One caveat: I cannot open the oven with it on. Synthetic hair will curl and singe when high heat is applied. Basically, the fibers melt. I *almost* made this ghastly error last night. I simply forgot that I was wearing a wig because it's so light and comfy. I was about to peek on some food that was baking when I suddenly remembered and recoiled like I'd burned myself. My heart was beating like a trip hammer. Thanks to Michael's label maker, I now have a visual reminder to leave the oven alone, which I appreciate beyond measure.

"It Feels Like Summer Out There"
January 26, 2015

I have no idea what the temperature is, and I don't care. It's warm. Really warm. Any time that I—the chilliest person in history—am outside without a jacket of any sort in January, it's warm. Sunshine and warmth are good for my soul.

I had my standing acupuncture appointment with Butch today. It was great, as usual. He gave me some liquid forms of my herbal medications to help with the giant pills that are hard on my stomach. We also discussed the fine art of cultivating the ability to not give a shit (his words). Oh, and there was acupuncture too. This time, both front and back and, for some reason, three needles in my right ear—none in my left—in addition to other places all over my body.

In the end, my tummy was settled, and my soul was soothed.

"What I Think about When I Think about Cancer"
January 29, 2015

Lately, I'm coming across so much information about what's lacking in our cancer care system. And I can tell you for sure, there's a lot. It's more medical intervention than it is care.

First, once you're diagnosed, there's an onslaught of information including resources available aside from medical care (acupuncture, massage, social workers, therapists, physical therapists, etc.). And it's great information. But at first, before treatment begins, I honestly had no idea *why* I'd need it. I still don't fully understand all of it. It gets put into the folder labeled "Cancer Intro Packet" and you take it home with the hundreds of other sheets of paper slipped in there.

Second, you get a lot of attention and care right at the beginning. Zillions of appointments, consultations, exams, and conversations with nurses that ask you to assign a number to your stress level from one to five. Then suddenly once treatment begins, you're on your own. You go get treatment; the nurses are nice and helpful, and then they smile at you as they send you home, telling you to have a nice day. Yeah, right. Let's trade places and see how nice your day is. Honestly, they don't really know what I'm in for over the following ten-plus days.

Third, my oncologist isn't really that involved. The vast majority of my care right now is coming from Butch and Sally. Butch manages the physical side and Sally cares for my mental health. I am so thankful for them. Without them, I'd be floundering. And I'd probably be taking far more prescription medications for every symptom that arises. That's not to say that I think my oncologist is a bad doctor, it's just his role. He assessed my condition, evaluated my prognosis, prescribed my treatment, and that's it. I see him when I go in for treatments. It's brief. He sends in his PA first. She asks me all the questions about how I did after the last treatment. I tell her all my symptoms. She scribbles. I like her, she's very nice. But I feel a bit like a subject in an experiment. Then my oncologist comes in. They lie me back on the exam table and each takes a side to examine. Simultaneously. Left boob, left nodes.

Right boob, right nodes. Switch. I feel like the stock car in a race car pit stop. They're gentle. It doesn't hurt, but it feels pretty factory-like.

It's been a few too many times that I've heard, "Chemo is poison. Hopefully it kills the cancer faster than it will kill you." My oncologist didn't say it. But others have, out loud and in writing. I know it's poison of sorts but it's also medicine that can save my life. And it's what I've got right now. I need it, despite not wanting it. So I will do it. But I continue to believe that there has to be a better way. Someday, we will look back on the barbaric trifecta of treatment options currently available and discover there's a better way.

I'm not sure why everyone feels the need to remind me that chemo is "poison." I know. I'm the one who really knows. Telling me makes me feel worse. It's like telling the person with major burns that fire is hot. I'd rather focus on the therapeutic effect that it's having on me. There is a reason I need to receive this medicine. And it's working: my tumor is shrinking, and it doesn't hurt anymore. I can comfortably lie flat on my stomach and not feel it anymore. It's a better, more-comforting thought to think about how it's helping me instead of how I'm really just dodging the bullets of the major side effects. I'm not trying to bury my head in the sand. It's not even possible to ignore the "uncomfortable" side of chemo. I just happen to think that focusing on the benefits and the reason behind having to receive such harsh medications is the way to manage the process of chemotherapy.

I've said a million times that the power of positive thinking is so much more powerful than people generally want to concede. I'm not sure why that's true. I think most people can acknowledge that negative thinking can make you have a poor attitude, lack energy and focus, become depressed, experience panic attacks, manifest suicidal thoughts, and more. So *why not* the opposite? Positive thoughts can help people heal more quickly, have fewer side effects, feel stronger, and have an overall better outlook on complete health after cancer. There is an innately strong connection between the body and mind. That's why the placebo effect exists as a thing. I like to remember that what we think about, we bring about. Remember, if you think you can or can't, you're right.

I dislike saying "beating cancer" or "fighting cancer." Ugh. That sounds so exhausting. I don't want to go through my days in a constant battle with myself. That sounds horrible. So, I'm prone to think of it as working *with* my body to return to full health. Do I want cancer as a disease to end? Yes. Do I want better treatments for it in the meantime? Of course. But I don't want to fight, battle, and beat. That assumes that people who die from cancer were somehow less strong contenders. That they didn't fight hard enough. That they got beat. How sad. I read headlines like, "LOST HER BATTLE TO CANCER TODAY." And I think it's an awful way to be remembered. We give such delicate care to the headlines when someone commits suicide. We'd never say, "Lost his battle with the gun." We say, "Passed away." Beyond that, most times we don't really need to know much else.

I don't like any phrase to describe me that starts with a medical term—"cancer patient," "chemo patient," or in the future, "cancer survivor." How about simply, "Erika."

"Life Happens for Me"
January 30, 2015

I'm not a big country music fan, but one Garth Brooks song speaks to me, "Unanswered Prayers." It's an older song. I can't tell you how many times over years I've thought of it when I realized that if I'd gotten what I wanted at the time, so many other great things would never have happened.

I think it's easy to sit and ponder "what if?" Well, sometimes that answer isn't a good one, because we are where we are for a reason. My daughter gets freaked out when I mention an ex-boyfriend. She thinks that if I'd married someone else instead of her dad that she wouldn't be here now. And she doesn't want to entertain the thought. I try to assure her that she was always going to be my daughter. Because that's how it was meant to be.

Even when we're disappointed that something didn't turn out how we wanted it to at one point, it doesn't mean that this is the wrong path. There's a reason. No matter how painful or disappointing. Sometimes I get to know the answer. Sometimes I don't. Either way, there is a reason.

I trust that there is a purpose for what is happening in my life. Always. Maybe it's to teach me something. Maybe it's to help me avoid something bad that could've otherwise happened. Maybe it's to awaken me to the gifts in my life. Maybe it's because something better is out there for me.

I've adopted the attitude that life happens for me, not to me. It's like when I was studying PR in college. We didn't call issues "problems," we called them "opportunities." It can be called anything you want: making lemonade out of lemons, seeing the silver lining, seeing the glass as half full. I like to think of it as seeing things as they are. Because in the end, it's only our own expectations that we attach to things that make them "good" or "bad." It's very peaceful to be okay with what is.

I try to release expectations. Of other people, of events, of outcomes. It ain't easy. Especially when you really want someone to do something that you think will make everything okay, like call you back, or say yes to your question, or accept a business proposal. Whatever it is, life is more peaceful when we stop attaching our expectations to the outcome. I think this is where cultivating the ability to not give a shit is helpful. I notice how much more at ease I am when I decide not to care. That's not to say that I don't put forth my best effort, but once I do, it really is out of my hands. Caring so much that I am disappointed by someone else's reaction or response has been my MO for a long time. And it's exhausting.

I've always been a type-A person—good grades, industrious, accomplishment oriented. It's not until the past few years that the concept that we are human BEings instead of human DOings was introduced to me. We don't always have to be producing to be "good" people. It's really freeing to realize that taking time out to sit down and read isn't a waste of time. Or that a long conversation with a friend about meaningful things is an amazing way to spend an afternoon. That's the good stuff.

What it all boils down to is this: Live in the moment. Be present in your own life. Don't think about the "what ifs." Appreciate the peace in life. Appreciate your gifts when you have them for as long as you have them. Nobody knows how long you will have them and often once they're gone, they're gone for good.

"It's a Love/Hate Relationship"
February 3, 2015

For as much as I've bitched about my insurance company, I truly am grateful to have it. I honestly don't know what I'd do without it. Which makes me wonder, what do the people without insurance do? Cancer has to be one of the most expensive diseases to treat, hands-down. So far, I've had about ten diagnostic tests, an outpatient surgery, an ECG, two chemo treatments, and a billion office visits. And I still have a lot ahead of me. When the bills come to me, and I see what the charges are, my eyes widen. That is, until I see that "Patient Responsibility" column. That is usually around $29 after the contracted discounts, insurance payments, and my co-pays.

But what about those people who don't have great insurance? Something is very badly broken, and it makes me very sad for everyone who has to think about how to pay for their treatment on top of everything else. I'm sure many people have to choose between medications and food. Or choose a lower level of care because they can't afford the best. What about the single mom who is trying to pay for a child's cancer care? Maybe she can't be home to take care of them because she can't afford to miss work. Ugh. The scenarios are endless.

I wish politicians would stop throwing around terms like "reform" and actually do something to help people. The media demonizes words like "socialized" and "welfare." But is "welfare" really a bad word? No. When you're looking out for someone's health and welfare, that's a wonderful thing. Enter it into politics and suddenly it's an awful idea. But looking out for our health and welfare is exactly what politicians should be doing!

Knowing that some people are out there suffering to provide what they need for their families is heartbreaking. While at the same time, many people have far more than what they can ever possibly need, and the gap is continuing to increase. Not everyone who uses social services are "moochers." It's funny how when the 1 percenters use the loopholes and tax breaks they're provided, it's considered savvy business. But when the disadvantaged use government assistance, it's "mooching."

If I could share my insurance, I would. If I had a zillion dollars to help everyone who needed it, I would. I think sometimes people don't stop to think that when we throw around percentages and statistics, those are *people* we're talking about—people no different from you and me. And people that our government should be helping.

Chapter Four

Chemotherapy, Round 3

"My Glass Is Half Empty"
February 5, 2015

Normally, I'm a "glass-is-half-full" kind of girl. But today, I'm looking at a glass that's half empty. I'm now officially halfway done with chemotherapy treatments. Today I had my third of six. Half done. Half gone.

My oncologist took a measurement, and the tumor is now one-fourth its original size. He can no longer feel the affected lymph node. I'm very thankful that the chemo medications are working.

Since my last treatment, I've been trying to find some new methods for coping with the side effects. I saw Sally last week sometime (my chemo brain prevents me from remembering when . . . along with many other things that slip my mind. I've been reassured that my memory will return to normal when I'm done with chemo treatments). She helped me with visualization and gave me a reading resource for guided imagery. She also suggested that I try calming, relaxing music without words. I used breathing exercises as well to ground myself and feel peaceful for the whole four hours I'm receiving treatment. I feel better today than I have after my previous two treatments.

I talked with my oncologist about using a stronger sleep aid and a stronger stomach acid remedy. He said that my liver function and kidney function look good, and my blood counts are good now and were also good on day ten (which is typically the biggest dip).

When I've been feeling so sick, it's often hard to remember that these chemotherapy medications are making me better. My conversation with Butch reminded me of that yesterday, and my exam with my oncologist confirmed it.

I like to recall a line from one of my guided imagery recordings: "Know in a deep place that you are better for it . . . And so you are."

Tomorrow, I will see Butch again in the morning. Then I'll go to the clinic in the afternoon for my injection.

I want to thank some people for all their wonderful support. Thank you for the amazing dinners, gifts, cards, and texts and emails, and social media messages. They mean so much. Even though I don't often respond, please know I appreciate them immeasurably. They really help me when I'm feeling like I want to say *"no mas."*

"Cancer and Menopause Go Together Like . . ."
February 12, 2015

I'm not sure what the end of that sentence is, but it sure ain't good!

Some of the chemo medications I'm on are also used for ovarian cancer treatment, so menopause is induced while taking them. That means, on top of the chemo symptoms, I get to experience hot flashes, mood swings, and spontaneous crying.

About 70 percent of the people who go through menopause on the medications will have a reversal after the medications are stopped. There's an upside and a downside to that. If it doesn't reverse, then I'm menopausal at forty-three. If it does reverse, then I will go through it again. It just seems rude to pile on.

Loads of Thanks

Thank you to those who've given such thoughtful help: countless meals, a ride to the doctor, uplifting reminders for the house, and a cozy hat.

This Round

I'm appreciating the recent beautiful weather. I've been out to walk a few times, which, while difficult at the time, helps me recover faster.

This round of treatment has been different from the last one, which was different from the first. It's odd to me that the symptoms are never quite the same. They're not dramatically different, but they differ in intensity. This time, I've felt lots more fatigue and strain on my heart. My walks can better be described as "saunters." And there really is no place in this neighborhood to walk on all flat—unless I walk up and down my cul-de-sac twenty times. Even at a snail's pace, my heart beats like I'm doing high-intensity intervals. I feel a little stronger every day and am glad that my sister Kerrianne is here to walk with me.

"Staying Strong"
February 19, 2015

I'm feeling better now. I can taste food again, I'm sleeping well, and my stomach is pretty normal. I am trying to use this time that I'm feeling good to get caught up on things without exhausting myself. I have my fourth treatment again in one week. I'm very thankful for these days when I feel well. My kids are telling me that I make myself laugh too much. Is there such a thing?

When I saw Butch this Monday, he suggested that better exercise for me would be light weightlifting rather than anything cardio. He said that I need strength and muscle mass, not so much anything that burns calories. So, I started today! At work, actually.

While I was waiting for the printer, I did squats. Tomorrow, I will do a more complete routine now that my hubby fixed our home gym weight machine. Nothing crazy, just light weights, lots of rest between sets, just to keep my muscles toned. There are times when I'm doing a lot of sitting around. I'm also still doing yoga which helps with strength, flexibility, and balance.

The weather has been amazing. A snowstorm here, some blue skies there, and some seventy-degree days sprinkled in. I love it. The fox and the deer have been around to visit. So have the birds.

Now that we've refilled the feeders, we've had lots of repeat guests. The big fat squirrel keeps eating the apples I throw out to the deer.

Kerrianne was here until yesterday. We got to do some fun stuff like teach the kids to play euchre, shop, and eat out. She and Zach went with me to Boulder for an appointment. She helps me keep my shit straight. I'm pretty disorganized in thoughts and to-dos these days. She's coming back over spring break.

I'm excited to set the clocks ahead soon. I love it when we start having a later sunset.

On the cancer front, it's about time for me to contact my surgeons again. I'm halfway through chemotherapy, so it's time to schedule my surgery. As it gets closer, it gets more real.

Thank You

I'd like to thank the many friends, neighbors, and family who have offered their kindnesses: movies, a journal, a gift card, cupcakes, a box of fruit, meals, taking the time to ask me how I'm doing, or offer help. I appreciate all of you. I love all the cards I get and the texts and emails and social media messages. Some make me laugh; others make me feel good to be thought of so dearly. I love them all. Thank you.

"Through—and Beyond—Cancer"
February 24, 2015

One of my favorite sayings is, "If you're going through hell, keep on going!" It came to mind when I was thinking about having cancer earlier today. Yes, I'm going through cancer treatment. Right through—no stops—directly to my life beyond cancer.

But on my way through, I'm learning so much. I've learned a lot about cancer itself and the treatments. I've learned about a lot of people who've had cancer that I didn't know about. I've learned a lot about friendship and the character of people. I've learned a lot about people's generosity and kindness. But mostly, I've learned a lot about myself.

I've learned how to empathize with people who deal with real struggles, most even greater than cancer. I've learned what it means to be truly grateful. I've learned that I need to be kind to myself. I've learned that my favorite cake bites have one gram of sugar—even the sea salt caramel ones. I've learned that people are kinder and more sympathetic when they know I have cancer, which is a bit sad to me because shouldn't we all be kind to one another, no matter what? Just because you can't see that I have cancer doesn't mean I'm not sick. Just like you can't see that someone is dealing with bankruptcy or job loss or missing a loved one or mental illness or the death of a child.

The day I was diagnosed, I stopped at the store. Some kid was bagging my things and asked me how my day was. I didn't hear him at first. Or rather, it didn't register that he was talking to me. I had so much on my mind. I eventually snapped to and said something like "Been better." His response was, "Oh, come on. How bad could it be?" Who knows, maybe he's had an illness ten times worse than I have. Or maybe he's never had a single bad thing happen to him and so he hasn't yet learned that life is hard sometimes. But it certainly made me think. You can't judge a book by its cover. It's trite but true.

Many books have stunning covers but disappointing stories. Some covers are gray with the most colorful story inside. Some covers are breathtakingly beautiful and tell an even more amazing story inside. Just like all the people I meet every day.

I recently read the book, then saw the movie, *Wild*. People have asked me if I liked it. It feels weird to answer that question. How can you say whether or not you liked it? It just *was*. It was her story. Her truth. Her journey. And she was brave enough to share that with us. All of it. I'm honored that she shared her transformation with me. I've felt that way after many books I've read. It doesn't seem right to judge them at all—by cover or content. Which is really how we should treat others. And when someone is brave and trusting enough to share their story with us, we should accept it as the privilege that it is.

"Two-Thirds"
February 24, 2015

This Thursday, I go in for my fourth of six treatments. That means I'll be two-thirds done with chemo. The mere thought of March being a few days away makes me nearly giddy. Back in December, March seemed so far away. Now, it's around the corner. One treatment in March, and the last one in April.

I called my surgeon's office today to get the process going for scheduling my surgery. That will take place about three weeks after my last treatment. I'll need to do pre-op stuff and have another consultation before I have the actual surgery. Plus, I still need to have another contrast MRI to see just how "gone" the cancer is. I'm always eager to see my oncologist and hear him tell me how much shrinkage there's been and how hard it is for him to measure because it's gotten so small. Music to my ears.

For the last two days, I've forgotten to take my acid-reflux medication on time, which seems like a bad thing at first. But I was so happy when I realized it was half an hour past due. That means that my stomach wasn't feeling bad enough to remind me!

My weightlifting is going pretty well. I'm not going to be a world-class bodybuilder any time soon, but I can feel that good soreness in my muscles from using them, and I'm feeling strong overall.

Chapter Five

Chemotherapy, Round 4

"It's That Love/Hate Thing Again"
March 2, 2015

I 've talked about feeling this way about my insurance company. But this time it's chemo. I do not actually love chemo, but I do love what it's doing for me. At my pre-treatment exam last Thursday, my oncologist said that after three treatments, my tumor is no longer palpable. He was unable to take a measurement of any kind. He had to remind himself where the tumor had been based on the location of the biopsy scar. I loved that news. The chemo continues to work.

However, I really do hate chemo's side effects. I spent most of this past weekend struggling to hold down my cookies. At first blush, it doesn't sound so bad—nausea. But even water makes me want to puke. Hell, even the antinausea meds are hard to keep down. And the recurring question is, "Are you drinking plenty of fluids?" I really want to punch my oncologist in the throat when he asks me that. No offense, but the real answer is, "I drink as much as I can at a time to avoid puking and starting the whole process of fluid intake over again." So, sure, plenty of fluids.

I've been having an uncommon reaction to the treatments: I get skin eruptions. Think pimples except they're open and bleeding. Not on my face but, this time, on my legs. Last time, my back. Time before that, it was my arms and abdomen. Butch tells me that it's the chemo seeping out of my body. He says that I'm lucky that it finds a way out instead of going deeper into my tissues. I don't want to know what it's doing to my insides. Butch promises me that we will get me rebalanced after the treatments are over.

I've watched all the TV I can handle. And I'm now convinced that I would crush *Jeopardy!* Not to mention *Celebrity Name Game*. *The Voice*, on the other hand, is one contestant show that I'll leave to the people who can actually sing, no matter how much I want to hug Adam Levine. I think I'll have better luck meeting him at a yoga retreat or a tattoo shop.

I've been reading a ton. I got some new books, and now it's time for a few more. I've read my new magazines too. There are a lot of hours in the day to fill when your body feels like doing nothing. I've been reading about that, in fact. It's a book by Deepak Chopra called *Reinventing the Body, Resurrecting the Soul*. Buying it was one of those gut-feeling things for me. I saw it on the shelf and picked it up like it was a loaf of bread, thinking, *I'll be needing that*. And boy, have I ever. It's all about how to reconnect the body with the soul, as the name implies. But what's startling is how we, as a society, strive to do the opposite. We convince ourselves that busyness is good, and so many other harmful habits of a hard-focused mind. He spurs us to live each moment as if we have all the time in the world. That's not to say that we should ignore issues; it's quite the opposite. Dealing with issues big and small is what allows us to focus on the important things. It's that mindfulness that will bring our energy and awareness back to the body. We are not our bodies, but we need them to be alive. And right now, I'm really pulling for mine.

"One Month"
March 9, 2015

Today is an important day for me. It's March 9—exactly one month from the date of my last chemo treatment. *One month*. Boy,

I thought I'd never see the light at the end of this tunnel. But there it is. One more treatment on March 19 and the final one on April 9. *One month.*

I saw Butch today for acupuncture. He said that he could tell that my stomach felt less tense and that he feels as though my body is feeling more relaxed and comfortable with being able to handle chemotherapy. That makes sense because my mind is also more relaxed and comfortable with it too. At one point, shortly after my first treatment, I began to seriously doubt if I'd be able to tolerate all six treatments. But now, I'm simply ready to do them.

I've always struggled with processes. Any process: buying/selling a house, job hunting, pregnancy. I've never been a fan of waiting; I just want the good thing at the end. In this case, obviously, completed treatment and a cancer-free future. But like most things worth waiting for, it can't be rushed. One of the many lessons I'm learning.

I'm trying to make the most of things and not just wish it away during this challenging time. It's not always easy. But when I feel good, I try to see friends for a walk or happy hour (minus the wine) or catching up. I've been doing yoga in the mornings accompanied by some meditation. I use my acupuncture time to meditate as well. I have a little bit of a creative side, so I've been trying out some recipes for homemade sugar scrubs. I also made homemade gelatin. It's so much better for you than the packaged stuff and it's just as easy—boiling juice and gelatin. I'm also in the midst of the passionate pursuit of planning my new and improved garden. Last year, I tried out my farming skills and I was actually able to produce some things we could eat—cherry tomatoes, green onions, squash, green peppers, basil, oregano, and thyme. This year, we're adding eighteen linear feet and a whole lot of new stuff, including echinacea and chamomile, herbs out the wazoo, and tomatoes, tomatoes, tomatoes. Plus, whatever looks good at the time.

Surgery Is on the Horizon

I have the date for my bilateral mastectomy/phase I reconstruction set for Tuesday, May 12. That gives me about four and a half weeks from my last treatment to heal and prepare. There's a lot to do in that time. Tests, pre-op appointments, imaging, and mental preparedness—as much as one can prepare for such a surgery. Butch suggested that I take some time for myself in there, so I'm going to take him up on that! My hubby and I are going to journey to my favorite local resort for a couple of days for some pampered R&R. I plan to rest, relax, and eat a lot of food.

Michael has been great about my whims. And trust me there are a lot of them. If I feel like Chinese food, he ventures out. If I feel like French toast at midnight, he obliges. When I say that I'm in the mood for potatoes, he buys red-skinned, twice-baked, french-fried, and creamed in soup. Then he watches me eat a few bites and push it away. He's been very patient, even when I contradict myself. At one point, I got very tired of ginger tea, but it was helping my digestion, so I continued to drink it, with an eye roll and some dread. One day, he boiled the water and got out tea bags. I said, "So help me, if you give me another one of those tea bags, I'm gonna . . ." and I went on with my business, mumbling under my breath. A few minutes later, I turned around to get my teacup and there was no tea bag in it. I said, "Where's my tea?" He just sighed, shook his head, and got out the tea bags. I'm a peach. I know. But he puts up with me.

Today, after my acupuncture, I went to the store where I found gorgeous tulips and one single, solitary, organic green tomato. I fried that sucker up and ate it with gusto. It was so good. I can feel spring in the air. I'm loving these longer days. I look forward to the Boulder Farmers Market and its squash blossoms, gluten-free pumpkin bread, honey-crisp apples, palisade peaches, fresh-cut flowers, and more green tomatoes. Most of all, I look forward to my taste buds returning.

Thanks

Thank you to the many people who continue to send cards, messages, letters, and gifts. I truly appreciate your care and concern. I now have the chance to practice my indoor green thumb thanks to my new beautiful plants.

h1>"Insult to Injury"</h1>
March 16, 2015

On Saturday morning, I woke up with a cold. Normally, a box of decongestants and ten days are all that's required to feel good again.

But this time? Good Lord, I feel like I've been hit by a ton of bricks. And I'm supposed to get chemo treatment number five on Thursday. These are supposed to be my *good* days.

Knowing that a cold will last as long as it will last whether I complain or not, I got busy looking up natural remedies instead of being annoyed. This morning, I spent ninety minutes preparing and using five natural remedies, and, surprisingly enough, I had all of the ingredients on hand.

Step One: Essential Steam

I put five drops of tea-tree oil in my bathroom sink. Then I got a tea kettle full of boiling water and filled it. I used a bath towel to make a steam tent, and I breathed in the steam until the water stopped steaming. I took breaks occasionally from the heat. Man, did it make my nose run. Success.

Step Two: Sore Throat Gargle

This mixture of apple cider vinegar, sage, salt, and water helps with swelling, pain, and may help kill the virus. It was disgusting! It tasted like a mixture of . . . vinegar and sage! But my throat feels better.

Step Three: Sinus-Clearing Bath Salt

I filled my tub with very warm water and added a cup of Epsom salt and peppermint essential oil. Again, my nose ran, and my chest discomfort lessened.

Step Four: Hot Ginger Tea

Yes, more of the ginger tea I complained about before. It's not that I don't like it, I'm just up to my eyeballs in the stuff. But I drank it like a good girl, and it did soothe my chest tickle. I was awake most of the night with a very annoying tickly cough.

Step Five: Chest Salve

First, I melted coconut oil in a double boiler until it was liquid, then poured it into a glass storage container and added fifteen drops of peppermint essential oil. Once it cools and reforms into a semi-solid state, I will rub it on my chest like a homemade mentholated topical ointment. I'm also going to put it on my feet. Why? Because my grandma used to do that, and she knew a lot of things about a lot of stuff.

I'm going to repeat all of these steps throughout the day and see how I feel. I could take over-the-counter medications, but I'm worried about my poor liver. I've been told that my liver function is normal, and my numbers are in the range they'd expect. But it seems like a lot to keep dumping on my liver and expecting it to keep up. Plus, I feel like those are temporary solutions. Acetaminophen may make me feel better but that doesn't mean the congestion has cleared or the cause of the sore throat is gone. I prefer getting to the root of the problem.

It's nearly eighty degrees here today, so I think I'll sit on my patio in the shade and get some fresh air. Now, that is something that definitely always makes me feel better.

"I'm Sick, Not Color-Blind"
March 16, 2015

I called my oncologist's office this morning to ask if this cold would affect my ability to receive my treatment scheduled for Thursday. The nurse said that I'd still get treatment as long as my blood cell counts are good. She recommended getting lots of rest and treat for comfort.

But then I called Butch's office, and he squeezed me in. It's evident from my voice that things aren't normal, which made Butch greet me with a smile and a "whoa!" We talked all about my symptoms, and he said that he would expect that my blood counts would be high on Thursday, given that I'm dealing with a viral infection. He said my lungs are clear, and he gave me herbs to take until Thursday.

On his way out, he said, "You must not feel *that* bad if your shirt matches your shoes. Plus, your hair is always perfect." (Which is clearly a nod to my "cranial prosthesis" and its ever-present sameness.) I told him that I may be sick, but I'm not color-blind.

Chapter Six

Chemotherapy, Round 5

"T-Minus 21"
March 21, 2015

T he countdown begins today: exactly twenty-one days until my sixth and final chemotherapy treatment. I was able to receive my fifth treatment today. My blood cell counts were a teensy bit low. But the nurse said that it's expected at this stage that they could be slightly low and not a concern unless they're *way* low.

I have to say, the human body is an amazing thing. Given how I felt the past five days, running a fever, having no voice, chest congestion, and a brutal cough, I was scared shitless that I would be unable to have treatment today. My body pulled through! I tried hard to give it what it needed, so it reciprocated, and I'm grateful for that.

Strategery

Today at my appointment, my oncologist said that I'm doing great—still no palpable masses. He's very pleased with how I'm responding. I discussed with him my upcoming surgery and gave him the date. I talked to him about the lymph node procedure that my surgeon will be doing. She has me scheduled for a sentinel node procedure instead of a full axillary node dissection. Basically, she will remove the first node that filters fluid away from my breast on that side, along with two or three more. In the past, surgeons may have removed a lot of nodes and analyzed them all to look for cancer. But studies have shown that women who have the sentinel node method performed were as likely to be alive and free of cancer as women who had more nodes removed.

I was concerned with doing the sentinel node procedure because I've already had a positive biopsy of one lymph node. My oncologist said that recent studies have shown that outcomes are similar for both procedures and that radiation of the remaining nodes is really the key in treatment. I already knew that radiation would follow surgery and have chosen that doctor too. So, we are staying the course.

I Can See Clearly . . . Then

I asked my oncologist about my vision. Frankly, it sucks suddenly. Contacts, glasses, light, or dark. Though I've had glasses since the fourth grade, my prescription hasn't changed in a decade or more. It seemed odd that I'd have a vision change that abrupt that wasn't linked to chemo. My oncologist confirmed that it is. He said it can cause a change in the shape of the eyeball. (Isn't that some freaky stuff?) The good news is that ocular side effects typically self-correct.

Many Thanks

Thank you to everyone who sends me cards, texts, emails, and social media messages, comments on my blog, reads my blog, and prays for me. I don't know what I'd do without you all. I love my new book, snacks, bag, gift card, and continue to appreciate the visits.

"I Wish I Were a Horse"
March 27, 2015

It's true. Last night at 3:30 a.m., a lot of strange things went through my head, including wanting to be a horse. What I was really hoping for was some relief from my cough that begins every time I lie down, and knowing that horses can sleep standing up, it seemed like a very convenient time to be a horse.

The cold I caught almost two weeks ago has developed into a bacterial infection. Not serious, but enough to warrant an antibiotic and to leave me with a lingering, incessant, nagging, annoying cough.

During the day, the cough is minimal. But at night, even after breathing steam, drinking hot water, receiving back clapping, and doses of cough syrup, I found myself awake wishing I were farm stock. Earlier today, I consulted with the pharmacist and Butch's office for a new prescription. I'm confident that this will get me through tonight, with the sleep I desperately need.

"Happy Easter"
April 4, 2015

It's going to be a gorgeous day here in the mile-high city tomorrow, so after we do our basket and egg hunt in the backyard, we are going to attempt a bike ride. It will be my first bike ride of the year. I won't be wearing any yellow jerseys at the end, but I'm sure it'll feel good just to pedal around and enjoy the warmth and sun.

I'll be making pork tenderloin for dinner with lots of veggies and potatoes. But first, for breakfast, Fruit Bunny. He's almost too cute to eat. Almost.

I'm feeling pretty good these days. The symptoms I have are bone pain and heartburn/reflux. I'm still taking an acid-reflux medicine every day, but I have breakthrough symptoms. The bone pain is mostly in my long bones (femurs and humeri). I feel it mostly when I exert those parts, but not when just sitting still. Sometimes, I forget, and I squat down to look at something on a low shelf at the store, and then I get stuck. It's not that I can't get back up, it's that the pain associated with standing again on my own is a lot. So, I need a hand up.

Earlier this week, I saw Butch for some acupuncture. He gave me some Chinese herbs to boost my immunity and we talked about how we can heal my bones and balance my system once treatment is complete. I also saw Sally for some much-needed talk therapy. It's always a big boost for me, and I love the drive to beautiful Boulder.

I was able to go to yoga class this week. I do yoga at home regularly but going to a class is a whole other ballgame. It was tough. It lasted an hour and twenty-five minutes. My muscles were shaky, and my bones were wobbly. But it was a gentle vinyasa flow class so it's good for me and will help rebuild my strength.

It felt good to do normal things again this week: file our taxes and enjoy happy hour out with a friend.

This coming Thursday, April 9, marks the end. It felt like it would never get here. I'm so happy, I just might give my oncologist a hug.

Thank You!

Many thanks to everyone who continues to send their well wishes and words of encouragement. I appreciate you all. I'm grateful for the wonderful meals, beautiful Easter lily, and care package.

"Party Like It's April 9"
April 6, 2015

I've been waiting for April 9 so long that I thought it would never get here. But time, as it does, marches on. I am just three days away from my last chemo treatment.

I saw Butch for acupuncture this morning and he said that next week, we will start working on strengthening me for my surgery.

I Want to Ride My Bicycle

I did make it out for a bike ride yesterday. It felt so good. I went only five miles, but I had to start somewhere. It was a gorgeous day, and I took some great pictures at Bear Creek Lake Park. Butch would like me to start doing more weightlifting. And I understand why, but it's not as much fun as being outside. I'm trying to be a good patient.

"Taking the Jump"
April 8, 2015

With every step I get closer to finishing chemo, that's another step closer to my mastectomy surgery. The closer I get, the more real it becomes. I really wish I didn't have to do this part. But I do. I have to. I was given the option of a lumpectomy by my surgeon, but with all sorts of cautions and caveats. And my medical oncologist doesn't recommend it at all. A lumpectomy is not the way to cure my cancer. It's just a partial step. My risk of recurrence would increase by a lot. So, mastectomy is the way to go.

It may seem like a no-brainer. For me, it's not so clear. On the one hand, of course I am going to choose the treatments that give me the highest cure rate. But on the other, once I made the decision to have a bilateral mastectomy performed, I took pause. It's permanent, and I'm only forty-three. I feel like I'm about twenty-three. Giving up a body part is a big deal. Especially one so noticeable and associated with being a woman. They're not like tonsils. They don't reconstruct tonsils so that "they look very natural in a bathing suit."

People have said to me, "Well, now you can choose the boobs you've always wanted." Well, guess what? *These* are the boobs I've always wanted! I like being petite. I am a runner, a yogi, and all of my shirts currently fit. I have made it extremely clear to my reconstructive surgeon that I want to be as close to my inherent size as possible while still looking natural. He tells me that he may have to increase my size somewhat due to the area of the chest that needs to be filled. At the same time, he understands my desire to look and feel like me.

I've never really been the kind of person to half-ass things. If I'm in, I'm in 100 percent. I guess it's sort of like jumping off a high dive: I'll take a deep breath and trust myself that I chose the right surgeons, and I'll be as happy as possible with the result. The song that comes to mind is "I Swear I Lived" by One Direction.

I guess it's harder for me to talk about than I realized. This morning, I opened my mouth to explain to a client that I'd be taking a medical leave of absence for a few months, and I started to cry when he offered his understanding and best wishes. (Dammit! There's no crying in baseball!) It's not as simple as "You have to do this, so stop bawling about it." I know I have to do this, and I will. I will also bawl about it. I'll try to mentally prepare myself (if there is such a thing). Trust me, I know I'm lucky to have cancer in a place that *can* be removed. Many others aren't as fortunate. I get where I'm lucky. But at the same time, I think this is where my learning has come into play.

Through the course of having cancer, I've gotten much better at empathizing—with other people and situations foreign to me, but most importantly, with myself. I've always been a "suck-it-up" person. Well, I'm tired of sucking it up. It's an awful way to force yourself to live. While I'm dealing with the reality of having to undergo a bilateral mastectomy to save my life, I'm also dealing with the reality that it will be very difficult, and I wish it weren't necessary. I will have the surgery because I can. Because I want to. And because I was given a choice.

Chapter Seven

Chemotherapy, Round 6

"Now onto This"
April 12, 2015

My last chemotherapy treatment was infused on Thursday, April 9. It's in the past. And now I'm managing the symptoms and working toward ridding my body of the toxicity of the medication. I will be having a contrast MRI in about two weeks to look inside and see what kind of job that chemo did in eliminating the cancer. My oncologist hesitated to say "cancer free" during my appointment but said that everything looks and feels negative (for cancer) and he thinks I had an excellent response to treatment. The MRI will give us more concrete results.

The last treatment has gone largely as expected. For the last time, I had a fever the day after (100.2, so no antibiotic necessary) and am experiencing headache, nausea, neuropathy, skin outbreak, weakness, bone pain, runny nose, watery eyes, and just a touch of chemo brain.

A dear friend reminded me recently that my chemotherapy is now checked off the list of lifetime experiences that made me wiser and stronger. Now onto this moment. I'm trying to stay present and not focus on the past. Since Thursday, I've been drinking lots of water, eating lots of fiber, taking long, warm soaks in Epsom salt baths, and eating organic, nourishing foods full of antioxidants to help my body get rid of what it no longer needs. The intention all along has been to heal my body, and now I'm finally able to let that process begin in earnest.

On Monday, I will see Butch. He is going to start me on a new regimen of healing. Until now, it's been a lot of maintenance and symptom management. He plans to help heal and strengthen me for the next step in my treatment process, which is surgery. From today, I have one month before that happens.

During the process of healing my body, equally important is healing my soul. Yes, cancer treatment wore me down physically, but I believe it's just as taxing emotionally and spiritually. In order to restore my soul, I have some things planned.

First of all, I finished my taxes today. That process isn't exactly fun or spiritually fulfilling but having them done sure is! Talk about a lifted weight. Done. Submitted. Paid. Accepted. End of story. And we saved more than we owe, so now, vacation is paid for!

The next fun thing is that I'm starting my seedlings today. Just saying "seedlings" makes me smile. I think I'll start calling my kids "seedlings." They may object, but it won't be the first time. This timing allows my seedlings six weeks to become mature plants capable of enduring Colorado weather before they get planted in the ground we're preparing.

Tonight, *Game of Thrones* returns for its fifth season. So, if you call or text or email during that time, you may get what the Red Viper of Dorn got. It ain't pretty. That's "me" time.

This week, I'm going to replace my bedding. That may sound weird as a spiritual healing tool but trust me that when you've looked at that same comforter and those dreaded sheets for as many hours as I have, you want to burn them. I probably won't. But I will be happy to relegate them to the basement storehouse of comforters from days gone by. I'm ready for fresh, new, and beautiful.

Last weekend, the Boulder Farmers Market opened for the season. I'm so excited to go. You know where you will be able to find me next Saturday morning.

If there's a better place to restore your soul than the best little gem in Colorado Springs, I don't know it. So, Michael and I are planning a weekend there later this month. I'm ready. It's so pretty and elegant with natural beauty of the mountains and the amazing culinary talents of the restaurants. There's shopping and exercise and the Garden of the Gods—did you hear that? Of. The. Gods! It doesn't get any better than that. I could go on, but my head might explode.

Shortly after that, we are taking a bit of a respite in Ridgeway to stay at the hot springs. We've been there a number of times, including when we got married in Telluride (the springs are between Ouray and Telluride in southwest Colorado—my favorite part of this amazing state). What's different this time is that we're actually staying there as hotel guests and not just going for a soak. What that means is that we will be allowed to soak 24/7 and not have to go home at eleven p.m. when the non-hotel guests must leave. I've seen snow, lightning, rain, and stars from those soaking pools, and it's always breathtaking. I'm hoping for a clear, starry night in early May.

I do have fun things planned with the kids too. For instance, we're going to camp (in a yurt) and go to some baseball games. Plus, just about the second that my radiation therapy ends, we will be heading to Idaho for a lake vacation, "featuring" Kerrianne. We vacationed in northern Idaho once before at Lake Coeurd'Alene, but this time we will be in a bigger house for twelve days on the quieter (and Coeur d'Alene adjacent) Lake Hayden. This time, we're getting a bigger boat and will have a hot tub and fireplace at the lake house. The scenery there is simply magnificent. And we had a superb lunch at this little Italian place on the northern shore of the lake that I definitely intend to visit again (and maybe again!).

But my spiritual healing isn't all about going places and doing things. It's also about working with Sally, listening to my heart, writing my blog, and dealing with issues as they arise. I'm reading a couple of great books right now. And I'm enjoying that time to relax, restore, think, and even repair my cognitive function.

"We either make ourselves miserable or we make ourselves strong. The amount of work is the same."

—Carlos Castañeda

Chapter Eight

Preparing for Surgery

"Bones and Seaweed and Mushrooms, Oh My!"
April 13, 2015

I saw Butch this morning for acupuncture. He's starting me on a soup three times a day. It's started with organic beef bones and contains shiitakes, carrots, onion, two kinds of seaweed, ginger, ginseng, and dong quai.

Here's what I found about dong quai: Dong quai is a root that has been honored and respected for thousands of years in China. This herb is used to treat circulatory, liver, and respiratory conditions and is believed to help balance female hormones.

That all sounds like good stuff for me. It smells okay, sort of celery-ish but strong. Butch says I don't have to eat the dong quai. I can just cook it along with the ginseng in a cheesecloth in the broth then remove it before eating the soup. I'll try it both ways and see.

Next, we will implement more of our plan to heal and strengthen me before surgery. He's got some more tricks up his sleeve. I like going to see Butch. He's not like most doctors; he's always jokingly giving me shit about something which he knows I appreciate.

So now I'm off to the store with my grocery list of bones, seaweed, and mushrooms.

"Metal Mouth"
April 14, 2015

Throughout my chemo treatments, I've had the taste of metal in my mouth. And OMG, it is awful. I never imagined it could be this bad. I mean, you think, "So food tastes a little off, big deal." It's so much worse than that. It tastes like there is metal *in* your food. Right now, it's taking everything I've got to hold down my morning applesauce (which contains all the powders of my pro-biotics and amino acids so that I don't have to swallow ten pills twice a day.) My mouth even tastes like metal when I'm not eat-ing, causing constant nausea. The digestive system can't tell that you're not actually eating metal. The brain simply says, "This isn't normal." And so, the body wants to reject it. I'm already down about eleven pounds. I can't afford to lose anymore.

I made the bone marrow soup last night, but it went straight to the fridge. I cannot possibly eat a bowl of seaweed bone soup now. Not happening. Not until food tastes like food.

I've brushed my teeth so many times. I've gargled. I've eaten super sweet things (pineapple). I've eaten really bland things (toast). It doesn't matter. The metal taste is still there. My stomach is upset. And the worst offender? Water. Yep, good ol' H_2O. It's the worst-tasting thing, and I'm supposed to have how many glasses of it every day?

People can be so insensitive. I've had waiters make comments to me about the quantity of food I eat when I'm feeling good. When I've gone for days or weeks with a combination of hunger and nausea in my stomach, I think I've earned the pleasure of eat-ing whatever the hell I want whenever the hell I want, no permis-sion needed.

I may look fine walking around the grocery store, but my legs are about to give out, so if I lean on the end of the counter, it's not fair to assume I'm being lazy. Do I have to take off my wig for people to be nice?

While I was online searching desperately for ways to get rid of metal mouth, a cross-linked article came up. It was perfect. I've had literally every one of these things happen to me—and more.

It was written by the Fred Hutch Cancer Center and offers insights on relating to cancer patients. The article recommends that five things you *shouldn't* say are:

- "What are your odds?"
- "You brought this on yourself."
- "I know someone with your type of cancer. They died."
- "Forget what your doctor says, you should try X, Y, or Z."
- Nothing.

And three things you *should* do are:

- Speak from the heart.
- Help with specific tasks.
- Remember, even cancer patients get cancered out.

"Detox and Diet"
April 21, 2015

I saw Butch today for acupuncture. He put me on some new herbs to help me detox before my surgery. And he didn't give me any new horrible, awful, terrible, no good, very bad soup recipes, which made me happy. We discussed my diet, which doesn't veer a lot from my normal diet: no red meat, no alcohol, light on dairy, and heavy on the omega-3s and fruits and veggies. It still floors me that he can take my pulse and say, "Oh, you're having night sweats?" How can he tell that? It never ceases to amaze. He assures me that if I were going to lose my eyebrows and eyelashes, I would've by now, so I *think* I'm out of the woods on that one. He also said that it's promising that I already have peach fuzz on my head. He thinks it's going to come back in curly and guesses I'll be able to wear a pixie cut by July. That would be really nice for my lake vacation in August.

My surgery is exactly three weeks from today. I'm so thankful to have this time in between to heal. And begin to feel normal again. I did yoga this morning at home and meditated during my acupuncture. I feel a little stronger every day.

I've Made My Bed, Now I'll Lie in It!

I did change my bedding this week. It looks so warm and comfy to me. But mostly, it looks new. I was so ready for a new look after staring at the same comforter and sheets for the last four months, sometimes for days or weeks on end. I've also gotten motivated to paint my bathroom. I chose the paint color this morning with the help of my friend. I'm excited to see how that will change the look of the bathroom.

"'My Thoughts Are Like Butterflies, Pinned to a Page'"
April 30, 2015

This quote is from a book I read recently, and it rang true for me. I feel that keeping this blog is a way for me to pin down my thoughts. I have a lot of butterflies floating around up there right now and my cognitive function is returning. Putting the thoughts down in words helps me make sense of things and acts as a source of my memory. I still employ the use of lists and rely on them heavily. When I need to recall something from scratch, I eventually get there, maybe not as fast as I'm used to, but it is improving.

Near Complete Resolution

Yesterday I had an MRI to see how effective chemo was for me. Keep in mind that chemo was never intended to be my definitive treatment. It was meant to shrink the tumor and lymph nodes that were positive for malignancy. Surgery has always been the plan followed by radiation. Still is. That said, the radiology report reads as follows:

1. "Near complete resolution of previous mass and non-mass enhancement in the left breast consistent with response to neoadjuvant chemotherapy."
2. "Decrease in size of known malignant axillary lymphadenopathy as well as decrease in size of enlarged intramammary node."
3. "Decrease in size of malignant appearing intramammary nodes."

"RECOMMENDATIONS: Appropriate surgical/clinical management recommended."

Hand-scrawled notes by my oncologist to his nurse: "Call patient. Looks very good. Significant response to pre-op chemo treatment."

So, this is all good news. The chemo did what it was supposed to do: shrink the tumor. And shrink it did! "Near complete resolution of previous mass." I'll take it!

My oncologist told me that it will be a month from now that my taste is completely normal, that my nose stops running, and my eyes stop watering. He said he knows it's not easy stuff, but overall, I handled it pretty well. Perhaps so, physically, but he wasn't there to see me on some of those mornings when my emotional bucket was full. But then, maybe that's part of handling it.

Immunotherapy Treatment

Today I had my first immune-targeted therapy. This is one of the medications that I received during chemo treatments as well, but I will continue to receive it for a full year, in total. This medication is an immunotherapy drug that specifically targets the HER2 cancer cells that are characteristic of my type of cancer. The treatment is given in the same way as chemo (through my port) and at the same interval (every three weeks), but it's not like chemo, in that it won't make me sick, my hair will continue to grow back, and it doesn't affect all my cells the way chemo did. It's more targeted.

So far, I feel fine. Other than not wanting to be in the infusion room again, the treatment was painless and quick. This one takes only half an hour.

Pre-Op Consultation

After my treatment this morning, I met with my reconstructive surgeon for all of my pre-op instructions, consent forms, prescriptions, and final questions. There was so much information. Nothing new in the big picture, but now we're getting down to ten days away and they're starting to get into the details of post-op care.

There is a lot to know and do. And I still really wish I didn't have to know or do any of it.

"One Week till Surgery"
May 5, 2015

I found out yesterday that I can have my port removed during my surgery next week. Originally the plan was to keep the port in all year while I continue to receive my immunotherapy treatments, but my veins held up nicely during chemo so they can give it to me intravenously. The infusion takes only half an hour, and it's not damaging to veins. So, the port's coming out. I'm so glad. It did a great job while it needed to, and now it can go. It's pinchy and restrictive and I accidentally roll onto it as a side sleeper. Au revoir!

I have a million and one things I'd like to do before next Tuesday; I'm gradually crossing off the list. Aside from the medical appointments to prepare for the surgery, I've cleaned and purged my closet, which gave me great satisfaction. I got my seedlings repotted. I've run a zillion errands. The last big project is to paint the wall in my bathroom.

Mary, Mary, Quite Contrary, How Does Your Garden Grow?

Mine is growing very well, thanks! All of this rain that we're getting is doing wonders for my garden soil. It's nice and moist and ready for tilling. And I actually have sprouts that will be ready to plant. I may have overdone it; I have forty-four plants of just the things I started indoors. I still have six or seven things to start outside once it's a little warmer.

Rocky Mountain High

One thing I'm not growing is marijuana. With a dispensary on every corner here, it's hardly necessary. Recently, I've been researching the healing properties of marijuana. The good thing is, these days, there's no need to smoke the stuff. They make it into oil, paste, salve, transdermal patches, sprays, cookies, gummy bears, and more.

I decided to give it a shot. I've been having a lot of bone and muscle pain, sleep disruption, and some lingering nausea—all things that marijuana is touted to help.

I bought transdermal patches and salve which produce no psychoactive effect (they don't get you high). They are good to use during the day for symptom relief and can last up to ten hours. Some strains have shown to have antitumor properties so that's the kind I got. The salve is really great for pain relief and skin healing. One testimonial I read talked about how the salve healed, in a matter of weeks, a radiation sore that hadn't healed in six years with other medications. So far, it has healed my thumb blister from raking way faster than anything in the past. I will certainly be using it for scar and skin healing soon.

Lastly, I bought a sublingual spray that I use at night. The legal dose is ten milligrams. The spray is one milligram per squirt, so it's very easy to manage and control the amount I want and need. It is a hybrid of indica and sativa (the two most common strains of marijuana grown). Indica is a mellowing strain, and sativa is more uplifting. My spray has more indica so it's good for inducing calmness and sleep. By the way, it tastes horrible. They've attempted to make it palatable by adding peppermint oil, but it really just tastes like skunk and peppermint. It does, however, work.

Hot Springs

Ouray was so much fun. We spent two days there last weekend. The healing lithium water of the spring felt awesome. I really wish I could've taken pictures in the springs area, but for privacy, it's not allowed. The morning was more beautiful than a postcard: clear blue skies, crisp mountain air, snow on the peaks of the Sneffels range as the sun rose and steam was rising from the roughly 110-degree water. A quiet few people enjoyed the serenity as much as we did.

After breakfast, we took a bike ride. It was slow going, and I lasted about ninety minutes. We didn't get far, but it was so beautiful and quiet. I put my glutes and quads to the test, and I was happy to be active and conditioning my body again. I had to stop often when my energy got sapped.

Thanks

Thank you to everyone who continually sends me cards of encouragement and everyone who comments on my blog, sends me messages, and texts me. I so appreciate all of you.

Special thanks to my parents for my massage package. I had one today that was great. It really helped with my muscle pain and the therapist even got my right arm completely extended. At the end, he gave me some stretches to do for my pec muscles to prepare for surgery.

"I Will Be Well"
May 9, 2015

This will be my last post before surgery, probably. Kerrianne is flying in tonight, and we have a fun weekend planned (Boulder Farmer's Market, Mother's Day brunch). Then Monday I get the contrast injection (for the proper removal of the sentinel node and any other affected nodes). Then Tuesday is the day.

I feel better about the surgery now than I ever have. I had an appointment with Sally on Wednesday and we did some guided visualization. She also gave me a CD and a book to help with a successful surgery. I plan to listen to the CD during surgery. The idea is to block out any unwanted noise, information, or chatter that my mind still hears during surgery, even while asleep. The CD is filled with positive affirmations including this one I like best: "I will be well—not out of a fear of death or disability, but out of the love of living!"

Yesterday, I talked to one of the nurses about my presurgical medical history. She was so nice. She assured me that I am in the best hands and said that they'd take very good care of me. I also saw Butch yesterday for acupuncture. He gave me some herbs and minerals to take as soon as I'm in recovery to help my body get rid of the anesthesia. And more to start once I'm home.

Today, I will meet with my surgical oncologist for my pre-op appointment. She has such a personable touch; you'd never know that she's a surgeon. (Ha!)

The surgery starts at 8:30 a.m. MST and will last for about four hours. I will stay in the hospital at least one night. As long as my stomach is settled and I can tolerate food, they will send me home the following afternoon (Wednesday). I've already filled all the prescriptions that were given to me last week, mostly for pain, sleep, and infection prevention.

This will be the longest that I will have been under anesthesia. I tend to get a little cuckoo on the stuff. After my port surgery in December, I was in recovery when the nurse asked me if I cared for a snack. I said no because I just had an apple. A little time went by, and Michael said, "Where did you get an apple? Did they give it to you back in the operating room?" I said, "What? I didn't have an apple." Apparently, I make things up. This oughta be fun.

I was thinking the other day that this is one stage of the cancer treatment that is over in four hours. *Hours* instead of months. Yes, there will be recovery time. But this major step toward my healing is over in a matter of hours. This is one area of medicine that Western practice does very well. I trust that I'm in the best hands possible. I chose well.

Thanks to everyone who has sent me messages of encouragement and positive energy. I'm grateful for all of it.

And now, I'm ready.

Prior to treatment:

December 20, 2014. I was given my diagnosis three weeks prior and was six days from starting chemo. That day, I had gotten several inches cut off in preparation for the inevitable hair loss. I was feeling healthy and happy here. I was absolutely unprepared for what was about to come.

During treatment:

My second chemotherapy infusion. I still have my natural hair, and I'd gotten wise enough to wear noise-canceling headphones. Over the six or more hours I'd spend in this room, I heard too much about others' symptoms, stages, and complications. Those thoughts scared me and could easily penetrate my psyche.

Once my hair fell out, I decided to get a wig. Ultimately, it was one of the best decisions I made. I felt and looked like me. People who didn't know me well didn't know it wasn't my own hair.

Every night, I took the wig off, brushed it, and it was ready for the next day. About once a month, I handwashed it with shampoo in the sink and it dried overnight. No muss, no fuss.

Digestion is one of the hardest-hit systems of the body during chemo. I experienced a rock-hard lump in the center of my abdomen, nausea, a strong taste of metal in my mouth, and nearly incessant diarrhea. Butch recommended a steady diet of easily digestible protein like fish or chicken, some simple carbs like white rice, and cooked veggies. I ate this meal three times a day for the first ten to eleven days after each treatment.

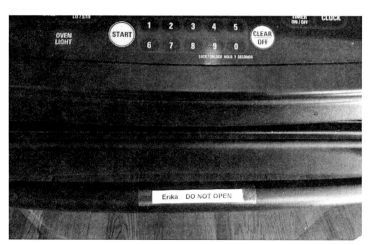

Erika DO NOT OPEN

My wig was made of synthetic fibers, which meant that it was sensitive to heat. If I were to open the oven while wearing it, the fibers would singe, curl, and maybe even burn. Michael made me this label to remind myself—often at the very last second! I managed to get through all of treatment without an incident and was able to pass on my wig in perfect condition to someone else going through breast cancer.

Once chemo was done, I had about three weeks to prepare for my bilateral mastectomy—both physically and mentally. Michael and I went to Ouray to visit the hot springs and get some R and R. I decided to be grateful for being in the fresh air, seeing the mountains, and relishing the opportunity to be alive. It was no longer about "getting in the miles."

Just a few days post-mastectomy. Kerrianne gave me some early birthday presents to help me rest. In this picture, I'm wearing an oversized front-buttoned shirt of Michael's because I couldn't raise my arms to pull anything over my head. I also had drains on either side of my chest to collect the fluid. My abdomen was distended due to anesthesia and pain meds.

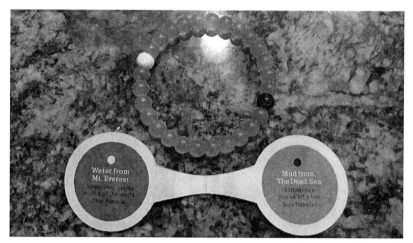

A birthday gift from Aspen, just two weeks after my mastectomy.
I love and cherish it.

Finding time and space to be quiet and alone was very important. Under this tree in my backyard was one of my favorite spots. I read, meditated, slept, thought, and enjoyed the warmth.

This is the paper chain I made according to the colors of the chakras to get me through radiation therapy. As it hung in my office, each day I cut off the next link, and while undergoing the treatment, I meditated on that chakra.

On my last day of radiation treatment, Michael made dinner plans for us. But when we showed up, a close group of friends was there to celebrate with us. By then, I'd stopped wearing my wig. It was August, and the wig was too hot for my liking.

Biking in Breckenridge. The nurse in my radiation oncologist's office nominated me for Domus Pacis Family Respite, a not-for-profit in Colorado. My family and I were lucky enough to spend a week in a condo near the ski hill.

Kerrianne had a Labor Day party at her house in Ohio where my family from all over the region came to visit with me for the first time since I had been diagnosed the year before. After I had written about cancer being in my rearview mirror in a blog post, my sister Monica got the idea to create a gift around the concept. So she got some rearview mirrors from a local salvage yard and made "Cancer" signs to complete the image.
I still have one of the mirrors.

Eleven months after my initial diagnosis, I completed a 5K run. But this wasn't just any race, it was the Great Candy Run, which my boss created more than a decade before for his Fetal Health Foundation. I was part of the race for many years as the Sponsorship Sales Director, so it was only fitting that this was the race I chose for my entrée back to the running world.

After treatment and recovery:

*About a year after my mastectomy, I got these tattoos: no mud, no lotus.
Buddhist monk Thich Nhat Hahn coined this elegant phrase to explain that
our own happiness cannot exist apart from our struggle and suffering. He
believed that like a lotus flower, our spirits can be at peace knowing they will
rise and bloom through adversity, emerging transformed and whole. I found
this worthy of a permanent reminder.*

Two years after my mastectomy and subsequent radiation, I was finally able to position my arm like this again. Radiation stiffened my entire upper left quadrant; the mastectomy tightened my pectorals and left me with upper extremity strength and spine imbalance. Physical therapy and yoga were key to getting my mobility back. I still work on it today.

Three years after chemo, my hair was long again. I used my hair growth as a symbol for the internal growth and recovery I couldn't see. Here I was living in Germany and studying the language, a dream I got to fulfill.

Of the myriad things I'm grateful for, here are at least four in one picture:
My husband, Michael.
The ability to travel—we were at Lake Como in Menaggio, Italy.
Oat milk latte.
Chocolate gelato.

I'm grateful for my dogs, Breck and Henry. Here we had stopped at a stream
on our hike, one of their favorite things to do.

My gratitude practice:

I'm grateful to be living in the Rocky Mountains again. This picture is at Lake McDonald in Glacier National Park. The mountains make my soul happy.

I'm grateful for my family: Kerrianne, Aspen, Michael, and Zach. This was December 26, 2022, exactly eight years after my first chemo treatment. A solid reminder that nothing lasts forever. This, too, shall pass.

Chapter Nine

Mastectomy

"Welp, That's Done"
May 27, 2015

I t's been a while since I've written, so this may be long. It also may contain lots of medical information—perhaps too much for some readers. Take what you want, leave the rest. I want to put in a lot of details about the surgery and my boobs because I know that I have some readers who are about to experience the surgery themselves, and I'd like to be helpful. After all, it *is* called *Blog about My Boobs*!

The Surgery

I opted for bilateral mastectomy. There was no sign of cancer on the right side, but the best predictor of future risk is past disease, so by removing the right as well, my risk was reduced by 98.5 percent. That's pretty damn good. Hard to refute a stat like that. Plus, I want my reconstruction to be symmetrical. I know that had I opted for a single mastectomy, my surgeon would have done his best to augment the right side to match, it just didn't seem like the best approach. Hell, I don't even like it when a picture frame gets tilted!

Before surgery, I had done lots of meditation on positive affirmations on calming, healing thoughts, so I wasn't nervous at all that morning. In fact, thanks to my awesome marijuana oil, I slept through my alarm. It was the chirping of birds that woke me up at 5:15 a.m. We still had plenty of time, but it was half an hour later than the alarm was set for.

The surgery went very well. They told me it would be four-plus hours. Mine was more like three-plus. Both the surgical oncologist and the reconstructive surgeon said that it was "textbook." Part of my surgery plan was to listen to music so that I could block out unwanted noise, chatter, and general talk about the surgery that my brain would still register despite being asleep. My anesthesiologist put my earbuds in for me and hit play on my tablet once I was in la-la land. It was instrumental, calming music (think Enya). And I believe it helped me fill my ears with soothing sounds instead of whatever was going on in the operating room around me.

During the surgery, she removed my breast tissue, but I was able to keep all my skin because the cancer hadn't invaded that tissue. It also hadn't invaded the nipple/areola complex, but because it is considered breast tissue, it was decided that it would be removed too. She also removed some lymph nodes based on where the contrast dye showed the sentinel node to be, along with three others. She said that all my nodes were very small which was an excellent sign, so she didn't have any pathology done during the surgery. She felt confident that the nodes were clean.

Then the reconstructive surgery team did their job of inserting the expanders which are temporary implants that help stretch my pecs and other tissues to be ready for a permanent implant. The expanders are put in empty but have ports in them so that they can be filled with fluid to the desired size over time.

PACU

I was told I'd spend forty-five minutes to an hour in the post-anesthesia care unit before being moved to a post-surgery floor for the night. Well, for me it was about six hours in the PACU. I don't do well with anesthesia. I don't even remember the first few hours. At first, I had some nausea. Then the pain was pretty bad, so the nurse was walking the fine line between controlling my pain and keeping me breathing. At one point, I was taking six respirations per minute. And they were shallow. Once my husband, my kids, and my sister were allowed in to see me, they all took turns waking me up with reminders to take some deep breaths and try to stay awake for a little bit.

I'd been given phosphorus tablets by Butch for my husband to put under my tongue every two hours to help my body get rid of the anesthesia. We did that, but I'm not sure of the success of that endeavor. Maybe it worked great. Otherwise, I would've been there longer.

Finally, around 6:30 p.m., my pain was around four or five, and I was breathing more and deeper, so they wheeled me up to the sixth floor for my overnight stay. At this point, I was starving, and my nurse offered me crackers and water. I was hungry, like for real. I sent Michael out for a cheeseburger and fries from a great little café on Colfax. Granted, I was still quite tired and not quite with it, but when I'm hungry, I know it. Michael fed me my cheeseburger and fries with occasional reminders to wake up and chew.

I was in an area of [the medical center] that they are remodeling into suites. My "room" was four rooms. And quite nice. Michael spent the night with me, and Kerrianne took the kids home. My overnight nurse was kind and very relieved that she trusted me when I said I could handle a burger and fries on her watch. I slept very soundly, being awakened every once in a while for vitals.

After a full breakfast and lunch, I saw both surgeons and was allowed to go home that afternoon.

The Surgical Result

I'll talk a little here about the breast removal itself. The first time I saw the surgical result was the next morning when the surgeons came to examine me. I will say that it wasn't startling to look down and see how I looked. I think there are a few reasons for that: One is that I've seen mastectomies before both in person and in photos, so I knew what to expect. Second, my breasts have always been, shall we say, understated. If I'd had breasts the size of volleyballs, I may have been a bit startled. But I wasn't bruised, swollen, or otherwise "bad" looking. Just adhesive bandages across my incisions and drainage tubes on each side.

The only incisions made were around the nipple/areola complex. That's it. They remove the breast tissue from there, they go up into the armpit to remove lymph nodes through there, and they insert the expanders through there. It's just one football-shaped incision on each side.

They put a gigantic bra on me called an iron maiden. Its job is to compress and help with swelling. But it just ended up giving me a blister and they let me take it off early (six days instead of fourteen). The drains are a necessary evil. They help rid the body of unnecessary fluid that results from the surgery and has nowhere else to go because they're in a closed cavity. They are uncomfortable, bulky, in need of around-the-clock attention, and are in place for about two weeks.

Sleeping at an Angle

During all of my surgery prep, it was never mentioned to me that I'd need to sleep at no less than a forty-five-degree angle for two weeks. Had I known, I would've bought one of those sleeping wedges for pregnant women. Instead, I slept on the couch with the backrest and several pillows propping me up. Luckily, we have a giant U-shaped couch, so Michael slept there with me, and we both had plenty of room to stretch out (we're rather long people). He slept there with me for all two weeks, until last night when we were finally allowed to sleep on a regular flat bed.

Yesterday

Finally, yesterday, I got my drains out, which was heavenly. It's hard to cover them up to go in public. At the reconstructive surgeon's office, they said that things look "fantastic." So, I was able to get my first fill of fluid in my expanders—one hundred ccs of fluid in each side. Surprisingly, it didn't hurt at all. I squeezed

Michael's hand like they were extracting a tooth or something, but that was just in case. I barely felt the filling at all. All of my bandages, drains, and tubes are gone, and I was given permission to shower and sleep in a bed. It's the little things that feel so good.

Now, I will get a fill per week until I reach the desired size. The filling did leave me quite sore today. Sort of like I did a hundred push-ups. The good part is that I have diazepam and marijuana salve to ease that pain. They overfill the expanders a bit just to make sure there's lots of comfy room for the permanent implant (especially if I decide to do radiation.) Then there'll be a step two and three for permanent implants and nipple reconstruction, but that will be months after radiation ends.

After the appointment with the reconstructive surgeon's office, I walked across the street to see my surgical oncologist. She gave me a copy of my pathology report which she'd already briefed me on over the phone. I'll always remember her words: "Good news . . . no cancer!"

The report says that my lymph nodes are "morphologically and immunohistochemically negative for metastatic carcinoma" and that my breast tissues show "no pathologic abnormality" and are "negative for residual carcinoma." Like music to my ears. I hung it on my fridge and gave myself an A+. She checked me over and said that things look great, so I don't have to see her again for three months.

We did discuss the whole radiation possibility. From the start, radiation has been part of the plan. The goal of cancer treatment is not only to get rid of current cancer but to prevent future malignancy. Just because I'm cancer free doesn't mean that we stop with my immunotherapy treatments (which will continue till December) or don't do radiation. All of the treatments added together give me an 85 percent chance of no recurrence in the first five years. After that, my risk is even lower.

I could skip radiation because, given my pathology and my original diagnosis, I've been told that I could poll the world over of radiation oncologists and they will be split 50/50 on the decision when there are three or fewer nodes involved. It's my choice. But

I can't think of a reason to skip it. Yes, it's probably going to be five days a week for five weeks. And there's a risk of skin burning, peeling, and general irritation just like from the sun. But to me, those aren't good reasons to start taking shortcuts. The treatment set out for me at the beginning is working. Let's stick to the plan. I'd rather take advantage of all the treatments afforded me than to look back and wish I had.

Butch

I see Butch tomorrow for acupuncture for the first time since my surgery. I'll be happy to get some balance restored. He called me one afternoon after my surgery just to see how things went.

Continued Recovery

For the full effects of chemotherapy to dissipate, it takes a long time. But I'm feeling pretty well. First, my taste is 100 percent. I can eat tomatoes and wasabi with the experience of full flavor. My eyes have stopped tearing. My nose still occasionally runs. Most of the feeling is back in my feet. My fingers still experience the hot/cold, numb/sensitive feeling simultaneously. It's getting better. My chemo brain was not helped by the anesthesia/narcotic mix that was introduced into my body. But, slowly, things are returning. The bone and muscle pain continues to be an issue. I've been out walking a few times trying to keep it all loose.

I discovered at the nail salon yesterday that my legs need shaving. And the hair on my head is growing back. More and more each day, I look like a spring duckling. As far as I can tell right now, it's going to be brown. I suppose that may change. I'll still wear my wig for a while, but it seems to be coming in fast.

To be completely honest, the surgery seemed like a walk in the park compared to chemo. Yes, I have physical restrictions for two more weeks before I can even start physical therapy, but I feel good. For me, I tolerate pain much better than sickness and foreign symptoms (like neuropathy). I stopped taking the narcotics after only a few days at home and have just been taking acetaminophen. Between anesthesia, narcotics, and diazepam, I was a hot mess. I tend to be lucid in the moment and seem like

I'm getting it all and taking it in (which I am at the time), but I don't remember it later. I kept saying to Kerrianne, "They gave me a packet?" "The grape juice was purple?" "I said I was aware of the directions and signed the form?"

Thanks

I have so many thanks to say that I don't know where to begin, and honestly, I'm going to forget some because I'm just a little overwhelmed. Thank you to everyone else who has sent me cards, messages, texts, emails, comments on my blog, flowers, plants, and meals. It's been so great to celebrate my health with all of you. Thank you for continuing to follow my journey.

Thanks to my kids for my Mother's Day gifts.

Thanks to Michael for a zillion things. First, for my five-gallon bucket filled with gardening stuff: a kneeling pad, tools, gloves. They're perfect: beautiful and useful. Second, for doing all the stuff that no one else can: boosting me up when I get stuck like a beetle that flipped on its back, for feeding me when I needed it, for indulging my whims, for sleeping with me at the hospital and on the couch when your own bed was an option, and for continuing to say, "Good night, beautiful." even when I don't feel so beautiful.

Thanks to Kerrianne for being here. For my card, candle, sleep mask, olive oils, meals, reminders to take my medicine, refills of water, reminders to do my "spiro gyro," reminders to eat probiotics, cleaning, doing laundry, staying on the kids' asses, driving, making lists, and for winning euchre with me. Next week: rematch for world domination!

"The Final Stage of Treatment"
May 29, 2015

I've decided to proceed with radiation. As I mentioned before, it is my choice because there is no concrete data that unequivocally shows that someone in my shoes absolutely requires this treatment. I am electing to have the treatment because of the chance of recurrence—radiation has been shown to reduce it by 8 to 10 percent. And given that I'm forty-three (for a few more days), I've got a lot of years ahead of me to remain cancer free. I want to look back and know that I gave it all I've got. So that's settled.

As soon as I'm done getting the fills in my expanders, radiation can begin. I have another fill next Thursday (June 4). At that time, I'll discuss with my reconstructive surgeon the details about how many fills I want/need to achieve the desired end result. Then pretty much as soon as that last fill is in, I can start radiation the next day. I just have to have a thirty-minute planning appointment to get my tattoos for the beams and get the alignment in the machine correct. I asked to see the machine while I was there, and it's bigger than I expected, but it's not enclosed. So, my slight claustrophobia will not be an issue. Plus, after the initial planning, I'm under the beam for only about a minute total for all three areas (chest wall, axillary nodes, and subclavian nodes). I'll have twenty-five treatments in all—five days a week for five weeks.

On Thursday, I met with a radiation oncologist that is much closer to my house. I really didn't like the doctor or her staff. I've been told that the most common side effects are sunburn-like: redness, peeling, dryness, and itching. Skin care is important, and her regimen is too strict for me. Other side effects are fatigue and weight loss, but overall, the systemic symptoms are virtually nonexistent. Her office doesn't address these things the way my first pick for radiation oncologist does. I think I'll stick with my original plan.

I met with Butch yesterday to continue my treatment planning. I'll resume acupuncture in June, going every other week. He gave me an herb supplement to begin to help with the night sweats and hot flashes. He also gave me a name of a product to use on my skin if I need it during radiation.

The Amazing Human Body

Over these past several months, I've thanked my body for its incredible healing power, and I continue to do so today. I'm continually amazed by the capacity of the body to mend. I'm thankful that I proceeded through chemotherapy treatment without major problems and that, in the end, it was successful in eradicating the cancer. It wasn't easy, but my body worked with the medication, and I'm grateful for the best result imaginable.

Next was my surgery. I'm only two and a half weeks out from surgery, and I'm fully functioning with little pain, no swelling, and no complications. Things are sailing along. I'll start physical therapy very soon to regain full range of motion.

I will ask my body to work gently and efficiently with the healing effects of the radiation treatment in this next phase. I am also confident that my reconstructive surgeon has the skills and expertise to provide me with the best possible cosmetic result ever produced.

I'm also thankful for what my body has done for me over these past forty-three years. I had two healthy, eight-and-a-half-pound babies that I was able to deliver with zero complications, and I successfully breastfed both. I've been active in running, yoga, biking, hiking, racquetball, horseback riding, and just about anything else I've ever wanted to try. In the near future, I plan to learn to stand-up paddleboard. And I've, currently, still been able to go walking and tend to my garden. Given time and support, my body will allow me to return to all my activities and more. And for that, I'm grateful and happy.

"Another Trip around the Sun"
June 6, 2015

Since I've last written, I had a birthday. I turned forty-four on June 1, and it was an awesome day spent with my family being showered with gifts and love and baseball.

Fill 'Er Up!

I saw my reconstructive surgeon on Thursday for fill number two of my expanders. This is one interesting process, let me tell ya! After the first fill, they will no longer fill the right side until after radiation is complete. But they need to completely fill—and even overfill—the left because it can't be stretched as well post-radiation and there might even be some shrinking of the skin in that process. It's likely that I'll have 100 ccs of saline in my right side and 460-plus ccs in my left (radiated) side for the five weeks of radiation. This is a detectable difference, but temporary. The nurse at the surgeon's office told me that one particular department store that also has a "rack" has a great breast cancer section for just this thing. They sell tops with slits to place temporary fillers. She also said that they have even better customer service in this area than what they normally provide. I will definitely be heading there once I'm ready for that. Right now, I can get away with a big T-shirt.

The reason that they don't fill the right side is because the radiation beam comes in at an angle and they don't want the right breast "in the way." I'm in the rare position of being able to keep it out of the path of the beam. Some women who are going in for radiation and have had a lumpectomy only, don't have that opportunity. In the long run, it protects the healthy tissue of the right side, plus it's only five weeks.

The nurse at my reconstructive surgeon's office said that on the day of my last radiation treatment, I can come in there and fill 'er up!

Then there will be six months of healing time until they will swap out my expanders for my permanent implants.

Rehab

This coming Tuesday is exactly four weeks post-surgery. Man, time has flown. I will start physical therapy that day. I'll be going to a place that is exclusively dedicated to people who've had cancer. It's specifically for oncology rehab. The nurse at my reconstructive surgeon's office told me that their therapists have come into the operating room to watch a procedure so they can see exactly what a mastectomy patient undergoes. They've gotten glowing reviews from both the reconstructive surgeon's office and the radiation oncologist's office. Both said they trust them implicitly. I'm excited to get started.

My range of motion right now isn't so bad. I've followed doctor's orders pretty closely, and I can tell when my pecs start to feel that I'm overdoing it. Typing is easy because I can pull the keyboard close to the edge of my desk and rest my wrists on the desk so that only my fingers have to move. Reaching for the mouse occasionally is no problem. I've done some cooking (today, I made a double recipe of cabbage rolls for the crock pot), some dishes, some planting, and all my self-care. It's pretty easy to get shirts on and off now. It's surprising how much your pecs/shoulders/arms are involved in so many activities. I'm trying to gradually increase my reach every day. I still need to go up on my tiptoes to reach a few things, but I can hang clothes on the top bar in my closet, reach for a glass, and I'm allowed to drive now.

I can feel that my spine is ready for a nice, relaxing twist. As a yogi, my body has grown accustomed to being flexible. Right now, it's not so happy that I'm being more rigid than normal. I believe that PT will get me back into twisting shape in no time.

No More Wig

I think I'm done wearing my wig. My hair is growing back nicely, and I predict that I'll even need to style it in six weeks or so. I'm trying to do all the things I know of to promote hair growth: scalp massage, inverting my head to increase blood flow to the scalp, and oil. I've been using a rich blend of oils that is typically designed for facial skin.

Additionally, the wig is hot. The wig itself allows some air flow, but the cap that is worn beneath does not. It's made from bamboo and feels like a really thick nylon stocking. It doesn't breathe at all. I have tried to wear the wig without it, but the weaving of the wig is just too itchy and uncomfortable.

It's liberating to go without. This winter when I first lost my hair, it was wonderful to have. It looked just like my real hair, and it kept my head warm. When I'd take it off for bed, I wore a hat or scarf to sleep in because my head got cold. Plus, I didn't like how the stubble rocked back and forth on the pillow. Maybe I'm used to that by now or maybe my new hair is softer, but I don't notice that anymore.

I also feel more comfortable with people seeing me bald. At

first, I was also sick, and putting on the wig made me feel better. Plus, people can be real idiots and take liberties by asking questions. I had some people (acquaintances and strangers) ask me if the chemo was working and what's my prognosis and if they caught it early. And when I answered truthfully—which is I don't know and I don't know and not particularly—they'd give me a pitied, worried look which really just made me want to punch them. In order to avoid the punching, which, evidently, is frowned upon, I decided that strangers and mere acquaintances didn't need to know such personal things about me. The wig helped me from having to explain.

Now, however, I don't mind saying, "Yes, I *had* breast cancer and now my hair is growing back."

In case you're one of those people who doesn't know what to say to people dealing with a severe illness, I have a couple of suggestions.

1. "I'm sorry that you have to deal with this."
2. "Please let me know how I can help."
3. "Hey, (insert name here) what's up?" This last one I like the best because people with serious illnesses are the same people they were before the illness, with the same interests and concerns. There is more to them than their illness. (Hang on while I hop down off my soapbox.)

While my hair continues to grow in, I'll continue to accept my son's accidental compliments. Last week at the Rocky Mountain Airshow, he told me that I look like Carol from *The Walking Dead*. Then last night at dinner, he said that I look like Charlise Theron from *Mad Max*. And he's not even trying to get cash or privileges out of me. He's making observations. So, if that's what I look like to his mind, then that's not so bad at all!

Thank yous

Thank you to everyone who reached out to me with birthday wishes. I loved all of my social media posts, cards, texts, emails, private messages, and thoughtful gifts.

Chapter Ten

Radiation Therapy

"One Down, Twenty-Four to Go"
June 23, 2015

T oday was my first day of radiation therapy. I will go five days a week for five weeks. The treatments are quick. I'm on the table for fewer than five minutes. The actual "zapping" occurs in four areas of my chest/lymph nodes and each zap is about twenty seconds. It's a fast, powerful treatment.

In order to count down the treatments, I think I'll make a paper chain of twenty-five links and cut one off each day, just like a countdown to Christmas. That always seems to fly by.

Lots of things have changed for me since I last posted a blog, and lucky for you, you didn't have to read about all of my waffling and decision-making woes.

In the end, I decided to go to the radiation oncologist that I first consulted with back in December. I really like him and his staff. He's young and progressive-minded. I only started looking around because getting to his office is a fifty-five-mile round trip, and I have to go every day. I was hoping for something closer.

Well, there was "something" closer, but not exactly what I had in mind. This closer practice has very stringent rules about what materials patients can wear (100-percent cotton only, which is very hard to find. Most everything is a blend). They also have strict rules about using zero skin-soothing products whatsoever for the duration of treatment (five weeks), unless you have a problem that occurs. Literally every other person I've talked to who has either had radiation or works with it recommends good skin care throughout. And this other practice doesn't want their patients to receive hands-on physical therapy during radiation. In other professionals' opinions, that is the *most* important time.

Big picture: that practice wasn't a good fit for me, and I could foresee lying to my doctor. I would much rather be proactive and prevent skin irritation and stiffness, etc. as much as possible. I would rather be honest and have my doctor work with me to make sure I'm safe.

My radiation oncologist has approved all of my products, and there are a lot:

- **Coconut oil:** to massage my muscle tightness (pecs) and lymph nodes.
- **Marijuana salve:** for scar healing and pain reduction.
- **Emu oil (from the adipose tissue of emus):** for moisturization immediately following radiation.
- **Tamanu oil (from a plant in the South Pacific):** for moisturization overnight.

Butch has recommended a good daily moisturizer that I need to order online because it's hard to come by. I see Butch again in two days. I have a feeling that he will start me on some herbs for internal tissue health. And I've been told to keep very hydrated during this period. I also bought some aloe vera just in case my skin could benefit from some extra cooling.

Rehab

On June 9, I started physical therapy. I can't say enough good stuff about the practice I'm involved with. For starters, they cater specifically to patients who have dealt with cancer. This practice is the only one of its kind in the country. My therapist specifically treats breast cancer patients. She does it as her job, and she teaches it at a local university. She's amazing. She knows so much about cancer, chemo, the surgical process, and the reconstruction process. She is educated in every aspect of my treatment. She has even been in surgeries with my surgical oncologist and my reconstructive surgeon to observe mastectomies and reconstructions so she can see what the muscles have endured and how best to rehabilitate them.

Most of my time spent with her is for manual therapy—all focused on my chest, neck, arms, shoulders, and upper back. She massages the tight muscles, she does lymphatic drainage, and she teaches me exercises to do at home to return to my full range of motion. I'm getting there. I can now throw things at the kids, like socks left on the living room floor. And, thanks to a smaller watering can, I am able to water my hanging baskets and de-bloom as needed.

I'll back up a little bit and explain for anyone who wants to know about the arm restrictions and muscles involved in a mastectomy.

When reconstruction is included in the mastectomy, the two pec muscles (pectoralis major and pectoralis minor) on each side are separated and the expander is placed between them in a pocket that's created.

For those muscles to heal and for the blood supply to reconnect, I had to keep my arms pretty restful. I could eat, wash, put in contacts, and brush my teeth. But I couldn't drive, cook, do dishes, fold laundry, carry more than five pounds, put on certain shirts alone, and my surgeon didn't want me to raise my arms higher than forty-five degrees—all of these restrictions for the first four weeks. I was allowed to reach slowly and progressively farther for items. But I was told to not do repetitive motions (hence no laundry folding or dishes. Shucks.). Therefore, once PT began, everything was pretty tight. My therapist said that younger women tend to have tighter pecs because the muscles are stronger than an older person who has experienced some atrophy.

The second super cool thing about my rehab center is that they offer yoga rehab. The therapist who does yoga rehab does individual sessions at first to assess a patient's mobility and progress in healing. Then she offers group classes twice a week to improve strength, postural control, and flexibility. It's a great opportunity to relax, breathe, center, concentrate, and regain balance in addition to regaining energy and stamina to function at my highest level while finishing out my treatment. It's a great bridge for returning to yoga after treatment. She also teaches from an emotional and spiritual healing perspective. I'm on the schedule in July and am waitlisted for an earlier appointment.

"Paper Chain"
June 24, 2015

I *did* in fact make a paper chain to count down my radiation treatments like I mentioned before. To be honest, radiation scares the bejesus out of me. It doesn't hurt. In fact, I don't even get touched except to get into position. But there's something about the fact that I won't see any cumulative effects for weeks, potentially, that freaks me out. It's like I'm waiting to see how bad it'll be. And that's an unhealthy mindset for me. I have some plans to change my thinking.

Paper Chain

The first is the paper chain. Not only does cutting off a chain link each day give me a feeling of accomplishment but the colors also have significance. I used the colors of the spectrum (ROYGBIV) because they represent the colors of the chakras. This way, each day when I cut one off, I can do my meditation during and after radiation while focusing my attention on the chakra of the day. I'm down to twenty-three treatments.

Balancing My Pitta

Step two is that I'm eating and drinking cooling foods to temper the heat that radiation creates. In Ayurvedic terms, I'm a Pitta dosha. Here's what that means:

Qualities of Pitta: Hot, light, intense, penetrating, pungent, sharp, acidic. Those with a predominance of the Pitta principle have a fiery nature that manifests in both body and mind.

With my fiery nature, coupled with the heat and dryness of a Denver summer, and radiation to boot, it's a good idea for me to eat balancing foods.

- Sweet fruits like grapes, melons, cherries, coconuts, avocados, mangoes, pomegranates, pineapples, oranges, and plums. The sweet taste is cool and heavy but also anti-inflammatory. It pacifies heat, satisfies thirst, benefits the skin and hair, and tends to be grounding, nourishing, strength-building, and satisfying.
- Bitters like kale and dark chocolate cleanse the pallet and improve the sense of taste. They tone the skin and muscles, benefit the blood, relieve burning and itching sensations, satisfy thirst, balance the appetite, support digestion, and help to absorb moisture, sweat, and excess Pitta.
- Astringent foods like legumes, apples, and cranberries can benefit a Pitta by curbing the heat's tendency to spread, toning bodily tissues, preventing bleeding disorders.

Today I made a pitcher of cucumber-watermelon-mint water to get me on the right path. I fill up my water container from the hospital several times a day. Somehow drinking through a straw makes me drink more. Not sure if there's science behind that or just that I like straws.

Good Old Butch

I'm going to see Butch tomorrow for acupuncture. He always helps me feel better. And I'm guessing that he's got some herbal remedies up his sleeve that I can use to help as well.

Saturday with Sally

Finally, on Saturday, I'm going to see Sally to talk about my anxiety surrounding radiation. She always has some good techniques for alleviating, or at least lessening, the fears surrounding my treatment. It's helpful for me to think of each treatment as a "dose." They call it that in the radiation field. In fact, the entire field of dosimetry is dedicated to the calculation and assessment of the radiation dose received by the human body. Thinking of it as a dose makes it feel like the medicine it's intended to be.

My Garden

Everything that I grew inside from a seed has transplanted nicely and is growing. And everything that I sowed from seed outside is sprouting. The other day, I looked at Michael and said, "We're going to have . . . *food!*" I know, I know, that's the point. But vegetable gardening is a relatively new thing for me so I get quite excited when seeds sprout and eventually turn into something I can eat. I love my yard at this time of year. The hillside is so colorful with its profuse blooms, the grass is so green (with no watering), and the annual flowers I planted are starting to grow and bloom as well. The leaves on all the trees provide me with my cozy little hideout and plenty of shade.

"Chemo Brain"
June 28, 2015

I've written about it before. It's a real thing. Sometimes it's annoying, sometimes it's scary, and sometimes it's funny. Today was one of the funny times.

I had the house to myself this morning for many hours. It was a perfect time for puttering around, cleaning, de-blooming my hanging baskets, and enjoying the quiet. I love my backyard, so I made some breakfast and ate it under my tree—scrambled eggs, strawberries, and a peach from the farmers market. While I was eating, I thought to myself that I hadn't had a "chemo brain" moment in a long while and was very happy about that. I finished up, went inside, and started doing dishes and cleaning the kitchen. When it came time to clean the microwave, I cleaned the outside of the door first, then opened it up to clean inside—and there sat the tray of bacon I had made to go with my scrambled eggs. I literally laughed out loud. It was less than an hour before that I thought that chemo brain might be a thing of the past.

The bright side is that it's getting better. The occurrences are getting fewer and farther between. I'm used to having very quick recall and remembering details. Now I have to search the web for simple things to jog my memory. My oncologist says that it does all return. Mental stimulation helps—writing helps, reading helps, word puzzles help.

The two main ways I'm affected are:

1. Not remembering where I heard or read something. Usually, I can say, "I was reading an article in *National Geographic* at the doctor's office, and it said . . ." But these days, it's more like, "I read . . . or saw . . . or heard . . . *somewhere* that . . ."

2. Words escape me. You know how when you can't remember a word that you know will perfectly express what you're trying to say? It happens to me. All. The. Time. Even simple words. That can be truly frustrating.

Sally

I saw Sally yesterday and we talked a lot about radiation and my feeling of waiting for the other shoe to drop. I've met some people recently who are just, well, giant asses about sharing their opinions about radiation. I was fully informed of the risks by my doctor. I'm aware. I'm not sure why people do that. It's a strange phenomenon when dealing with cancer. Suddenly everyone's an expert. I've never heard anyone say, "You're having surgery? Oh my! Did you know that you can *die* from the anesthesia?"

Sally calls these "thought viruses." Depending on who says them, they can be very powerful. In fact, the more credibility a person has, the easier it is to adopt their way of thinking.

My radiation oncologist has been pretty great about being positive. He informed me of the risks the way a surgeon informs a patient of the risks of surgery/anesthesia. Yes, they're possible. But probable? No. However, I am legally required to be made aware. Now I am.

I think I'm done telling people that I'm currently doing radiation treatment. At least people whom I don't really trust with that information. Instead, I'm going to tell people the truth when they ask. And that truth is, "I'm almost finished with cancer treatment." End of story. No more thought viruses here.

Sally has taught me that it's impossible to *not* think about something that you're told not to think about. For instance, if I were to say, "Don't picture a yellow SUV," suddenly that's all you *can* picture. Sally says that when my mind starts to drift worrying about potential side effects, acknowledge it, then picture my backyard and all of its green, leafy serenity. And the calmness I feel when I eat my scrambled eggs under the tree.

Yoga

Tomorrow morning, I'm going to do yoga! It's been so long. I'm very excited. I'll be doing it with the physical therapist/yoga instructor I talked about before, at eight a.m. sharp. I'll be up when the magpies see fit, so it'll be no problem to make the first appointment of the day.

I Am

I have a new favorite song. It's AWOL Nation's "I Am." It resonates to the core of me. What is life but a series of experiences that continue to evolve your soul? Give it a listen online.

"Gratitude, Expressed"
July 3, 2015

In June, I drove 942 miles to doctors' appointments. In July, there will be more, probably a lot more. I'm keeping track for tax purposes. The financial side of having a serious illness is as sobering as the disease itself. And I'm lucky because I have great insurance. But before the Affordable Care Act, I might've been screwed.

Before Obamacare, insurance companies were allowed to limit your annual benefit. They could cap it at $500,000 or a million—whatever they could get people to agree to. It sounds like a lot of money, lots of coverage, but it's so insufficient it's laughable. I haven't added it all up, but I've done a quick calculation in my head.

Each of my six chemo treatments costs $60,000, so that's

$360,000 right there. Then I had surgery in May. I haven't gotten all the bills in for that yet, but one that sticks in my mind is the overnight hospital stay (just the hospital—no doctors, no lab, no anesthesia) for $137,000. Yep, that's right. For one night in the hospital. And that was just a surgery floor, not even intensive care. Now I'm doing thirty days of radiation. I have no idea what that will cost yet. Toss in all the office visits, tests, images, medications, lab work, wig, physical therapy, and more surgery later this year and I will have no doubt reached well over a million dollars in medical expenses.

Somewhere in the middle of May, I reached my annual out-of-pocket maximum, so I will owe nothing for the rest of the year. But prior to Obamacare, I could be paying for *everything* over the annual benefit maximum. Crazy. In the past, people would decide to end treatment early or delay it because their insurance coverage for the year was up.

The system is seriously messed up. Quite seriously. But I am grateful that Obamacare has given me and many other people the peace of mind to choose our health care based on what it should be based on—medical decisions, not financial ones.

Yoga

I went to yoga on Monday, and it was great. My therapist walked me through a sequence of poses that felt amazing. It's been a long time since I've done them, and I was afraid I might injure myself due to my surgery. But she assured me that by six weeks post-mastectomy, everything is healed, the sutures, the muscles, etc., so I could do these things that I was tentative about.

There is still room to improve, of course, but now that I am seven weeks post-surgery, I did a downward-facing dog, supine twist, devotional child's pose, and more (twelve in all). I am grateful for that. I brought home a sheet of these poses to do every day to keep me loose and continue to improve my range of motion.

Complete Pathological Response

Yesterday at radiation, I started talking with the patient who has her treatment in the time slot following mine every day. She's a very nice woman and she, too, is dealing with breast cancer. We are at about the same timing—both having had chemo first, then surgery, and now radiation. She's just about ten treatments ahead of me.

I was stunned and saddened when she told me that her chemo didn't get rid of the disease. It's in her bones. They're radiating her spine in addition to the chest/lymph areas. During her surgery, they took ten nodes. All ten tested positive.

Not that I wasn't grateful before but meeting a person in my shoes who sees the same oncologist that I do who is facing such a worse outcome was humbling. At the very least, she has more treatment ahead, more images, more medications. I feel extremely grateful to have had a complete pathological response (or CPR as it's known in the oncology world) and no metastases. Really, grateful doesn't fully express how I feel. But it's a start.

I've always said that I don't want to feel sorry for myself because there will always be someone worse off than me—no matter what.

"One-Third Done"
July 7, 2015

As of this morning's treatment, I am one-third finished with radiation treatment. I'll have thirty treatments in all. So that means I've completed ten.

I have decided to do an extra five days of treatment known as "scar boost." This part of treatment will focus specifically on the scar area and the skin a few centimeters around it. This is where the majority of recurrences happen. The reason for the "boost" word in the title is because the amount of radiation delivered is increased.

So far, I feel just fine, no different from normal. In fact, I feel a little better every day. I'm regaining my range of motion, my stamina, and my muscle tone. My weight is back to where it was prior to this diagnosis. (I lost ten-plus during chemo). I do yoga every day, at least once. And I walk to help reset my cardiovascular fitness.

I have a routine every morning: wake up, turn on the Tour de France, watch for a while from bed. Then I get up and do yoga on my mat in front of the TV, have breakfast, make the bed, etc. till the end of the stage, then I get ready for radiation at 10:45 a.m.

"Cancer Treatment Is a Marathon, Not a Sprint"
July 15, 2015

It's been a little more than seven months since I was diagnosed with cancer, and I'm barely one-third of the way through the treatment process.

Yes, a lot has happened in these first months: chemo, bilateral mastectomy, and a complete pathologic response. But it's far from over for me. I'm just a little over halfway done with radiation. Then I will need to get my right side fully expanded over the course of about six weeks. I'll still be seeing my physical therapist through the end of radiation and through the tissue expansion process. I'll still be seeing Butch for acupuncture during this time as well. And until January, I'll still get an immunotherapy infusion every three weeks. Then a second surgery is on the horizon, which means a second recovery process. And lastly, a third surgery probably around next May. In all, my treatment will take about eighteen months.

I think a good analogy is a wild party. It takes no time at all to invite people, have a blast, and make a mess. It does, however, take a very long time to clean up and repair the damage. That's the part that drags on. That seems endless.

At the beginning of treatment, I was told that I could have certain side effects from the chemo medications. I did—my hair fell out, my fingernails turned nasty shades and got brittle, my teeth became sensitive, my digestion was disrupted, my fingers and feet experienced neuropathy, my bones and muscles ached to the point of inactivity, and more. And it all happened pretty quickly. For every side effect that I cannot visualize (digestion), there's one that I can (hair loss). I use the ones that I can see to remind myself that it's *all* getting better, if slowly. I can't see my stomach lining healing, but I can see my nails growing back to their normal color and becoming stronger. They're my benchmark. As each day passes and I get longer, denser, fuller hair, I know that the same processes are taking place internally.

I think that for the medical community, the beginning part of treatment is the most crucial. They want to treat cancer aggressively. And I understand why. I just wish they wanted to treat the whole process equally as aggressively.

My radiation oncologist does seem to notice that this is a long and arduous process. Every Thursday a massage therapist comes to his clinic and gives every patient who wants one a massage. For free. We're not even *allowed* to tip. Rest assured that I sign up for that 11:15 a.m. spot every week. They also offer free acupuncture, but I was already being treated by Butch when this opportunity came along. They have a nutritionist who comes in once a week to weigh us, talk about our gain/loss, and counsel us in good nutrition (hydration and protein are key during radiation).

Lastly, his clinic is involved with a program called Domus Pacis which offers a week vacation in the mountains of Summit County, Colorado, to patients who need/can take a vacation. My family was nominated. We're in the process now of filing the paperwork they require. We were supposed to go to Coeur d'Alene, Idaho, in August, but my radiation treatment won't be done in time, so we had to cancel. Having the opportunity to have a week in the mountains instead is a great consolation. I'm thankful to the practice for nominating me.

"Hakuna Matata"
July 19, 2015

At yoga last Friday, the instructor made "Hakuna Matata" the theme for our practice. In Swahili, it loosely translates to "No worries." Her idea was to bring joy into the practice and not worry about other things, whether it be work or traffic or even how fully we were able to express the poses. Just relax and be problem-free. We practiced breathing fully and calming our minds, even doing lion's pose to release the stress before we began our asana.

She iterated a point that I wholeheartedly agree with: she said that in traveling around, she's found people in some of the most remote and underprivileged areas to be the happiest, the most joyful. I've experienced this myself. I'm not sure if it's the simplicity of their lives or the connectedness with which they live, but I've witnessed a peaceful, relaxed contentment that is rare to find here in the US. Most of the time, people are stressed and rushing. Barely cognizant of others around them, unless to be annoyed that everyone else is on the road at the same time.

I have found myself getting frazzled and overwhelmed lately too. I've got a lot on my plate right now. I'm finishing radiation which has me driving in heavy traffic daily. Plus, I'm anticipating the remainder of the reconstruction process and hoping it all goes well. Then there's my daughter's senior year, college choices, our pending move, and the possibilities of a new job for me in our new state. All good things. All stressful in their own way.

I keep reminding myself to take one day at a time. And remember to say no when I really want to. Sometimes, I want to retreat to the jungle and live peacefully with happy, carefree people. I'm reminded of a saying that an old friend used to tell me: it's not where you live, it's how you live. So, while the jungle is amazing and I will go back, I am trying to bring that feeling of joy and calm here. It should be spread everywhere and not be just a place to retreat to.

"Yet"
July 31, 2015

"Yet" is such a powerful word when you think about it. I haven't run a marathon yet. I haven't been to Croatia yet. I don't own a bed-and-breakfast yet.

There's so much possibility borne by the word "yet." Without it, the door seems closed.

I love answering questions with "yet." It's amazing how many conversations that phrase can open. It's a great little word.

I Will Be Positive and Persistent

Today, I bought a new bag for my yoga mat. It has the colors and symbols of the chakras on it, perfect for how I'm using the chakras to keep my radiation treatment positive and focused.

When I was cleaning out my former bag, I found a small slip of paper in the outside pocket from one of my regular yoga classes from before cancer. It said, "I will be positive and persistent." I had used it as a mantra for class to set as our intention. I'm glad I found it today. I went to yoga class earlier, and I found myself feeling frustrated afterward. It wasn't anything to do with the class per se. I was frustrated with my ability to fully express poses these days.

Right now, I'm two treatments away from finishing radiation therapy. So, parts of my skin are screaming red, like a terrible sunburn. The worst place is my left armpit—a pretty unfortunate place to have a burn. Every arm movement causes friction. And all of the creams and ointments I'm using make it sticky. The skin is tight and sore. I've been given a special medical-grade honey ointment to put on it. It's 80 percent honey and is used for burn patients and diabetic wounds. I've also been given a prescription antibiotic ointment to prevent infection. It's not currently infected, but the skin is cracked so it's a good idea to prevent it from happening.

Because of the radiation, and because of the continuing muscle restrictions I have from my mastectomy, doing yoga postures that I've been doing for a decade have suddenly become out of reach. I can't do side-angle pose, triangle pose, warrior-one pose, even child's pose, like I used to. Yoga has always been a fun challenge; it has always felt good. Now, sometimes, it hurts. And I have to back off. I have to modify—a lot.

Finding this mantra today reminded me to be positive. Be persistent. And most of all—say, "I can't do side-angle pose . . . yet."

Namaste.

"Joy to the World!"
August 3, 2015

One treatment left. I made it! I thought it would *never* end. This has been a busy, even hectic, summer. Tomorrow, I'll have my last treatment, then the doctor will meet with me, as he does with all patients on their final day.

Today I met with the nurse. My weight is steady, in fact, I gained a pound. (Thanks to dining out and parties for that.) My skin is continuing to heal in the way that sunburns do, slowly and with flaking, dryness, and tenderness. It's really just the left armpit that hurts. The rest is just a little pink.

After radiation, I'll go to physical therapy once a week, acupuncture every other week, and receive immunotherapy infusions every third week. I'm not sure how long the PT will last. I guess I'll go as long as my insurance will pay, and if I think that's not long enough, I'll pay out-of-pocket. I'll see Butch for as long as I live in Denver. He has a protocol for me to follow for tumor suppression and healing from treatment. The infusions will last till early January. I'll continue to have manual therapy and yoga.

My next step is to meet with an exercise scientist at the oncology rehab center to help me regain strength, endurance, cardiovascular performance, and overall fitness. She has a bachelor's degree in sport and exercise science, a doctorate of PT, and special certification from Rocky Mountain Cancer Rehabilitation Institute (RMCRI). In short, they help people who are recovering from cancer do so with prescriptive exercise rehabilitation and nutritional intervention.

I really want to be able to do all of the things I love again (run, bike, hike, yoga) and try some new things I've been wanting to (stand-up paddleboarding and SUP yoga). I figure I'll just go right ahead and get ripped! It should be easy enough. I don't have any fat to lose, so I should be able to tone and strengthen.

My hair is coming in nicely at three months post-chemo. I kind of like it short. I won't leave it short because I really love the flexibility of long hair, but while it's short, I'll relish the benefits of easy care and maintenance.

Chapter Eleven

Rebound and Fitness

"Yin and Yang"
August 6, 2015

I went to Butch this morning for acupuncture. It felt so good to hear him say that I look "terrific" because he's saying it from a medical standpoint, not from a cosmetic standpoint. He said that my yin energy is low, so he gave me an herbal supplement of tang kuei and Tribulus combination. He said that it would help with my skin repair after radiation.

I understood generally what he meant because I've been doing acupuncture for a while. I know that the intention is to balance the body's energy. There's yin energy and yang energy. I knew that yin meant cold, watery, and so yang must mean hot, fiery. But I searched it to learn more. Here's the low down, if you're interested, from the website Nations Online:

> The basic idea of the "yin-yang theory" consists of two natural, complementary, and contradictory forces in our universe, the principle of opposite polarity and duality. Both of the forces are different, but in the best way, they mutually complement each other.
>
> **Yin characteristics:** passive, negative, darkness, earth, north slope, cloudy, water, softness, female, moisture, nighttime,

downward seeking, slowness, consuming, cold, odd numbers, and docile aspects of things.

Yang characteristics: active, positive, brightness, heaven, south slope, sunshine, fire, hardness, male, dryness, daytime, upward seeking, restless, producing, hot, even numbers, and dominant aspects of things.

It makes sense why my yin would be low right now. I just finished six weeks of daily radiation in ninety-plus degree heat and intense sun in the high-plains desert. My skin is dry and a little burned. The medicines of chemo have affected my skin. My eyes are dry from chemo. Generally, cancer treatment is harsh on the tissues and blood.

This is where the tang kuei and Tribulus combination comes in, according to the Eagle Herbs website:

This is essentially a formula for dry skin that itches. To get to the root cause of this condition, one must nourish the blood. This is not as quick a fix as something topical for itching, but when the benefits do arrive, they will last longer than the periodic applications of topical anti-itch creams.

I just started it today, so it will be a while before I see any changes. But I like the idea of correcting a problem at the source and not treating a symptom.

Eyes Can See Clearly Now

Then it was off to the eye doctor. I've been a little worried about this appointment because, during chemo, my vision worsened sort of suddenly. My oncologist informed me that my type of chemo can cause a change in the shape of the eyeball (astigmatism), which is usually temporary. Mine seemed to have gotten better but I wasn't quite sure if it was better or I had just gotten used to it.

Turns out that my eyes are the same as they were before. She did a full exam including photos of the optic nerve and macula which showed to be the same as they were in 2010, the last time I had the photos done.

TGIFriday

Tomorrow is the first weekday since June 17 that I've had no medical appointments. Tomorrow, I have yoga at one in the afternoon. Then in the evening, I will spend time with my family. It's nice knowing that these days will be my new normal, again.

"How Wild It Is, to Let It Be"
August 22, 2015

Amid all of the hiking, biking, yoga, dinners, off-roading, cycling races, and other fun times with my family lately, there have been some doctors' appointments and continuing rehab.

Last week, I saw my oncologist for my infusion, my radiation oncologist for a skin check, my reconstructive surgeon for more tissue expansion, Butch for acupuncture, and my physical therapist for more manual therapy. I feel really well, and I am very happy to be done with the apex of my treatment. Chemo is done, mastectomy is done, radiation is done. Those are the big three. And while I'm glad they're done, and they've been incredibly successful, I'm a little scared because they're done.

That may sound strange, but during treatment, it felt like I was actively doing everything I could to get better. I was in the process of healing, eliminating, improving. Now I have to have faith that what I did was enough. And that what I'm currently doing is enough. And that all that I'll continue to do will be enough.

I am reminded of the final paragraph of *Wild* by Cheryl Strayed. She says, "*It was all unknown to me then, as I sat on that white bench on the day I finished my hike. Everything except the fact that I didn't have to know. That it was enough to trust that what I'd done was true. To understand its meaning without yet being able to say precisely what it was . . .*"

That's where I am: sitting on my own white bench of sorts, after I've finished my treatment, knowing that it is enough to trust that what I've done is true.

Strayed summarizes, "*How wild it is, to let it be.*"

"The Body Is Your Temple"
August 28, 2015

Yoga master B. K. S. Iyengar has been quoted as saying, *"The body is your temple. Keep it pure and clean for your soul to reside in."* I'm really working on it.

This morning's cardiorespiratory fitness test provided me with a wellspring of useful information.

My therapist explained that the medical practice of rehabilitating people who've had cancer is quite new. However, whenever someone has a heart attack, one of the first things that is prescribed is cardiac rehab. That's after damage to one muscle. Chemo damages every system. Most recovering cancer patients are expected to care enough to piece together help, do it on their own, or, sadly, most commonly, do nothing to regain fitness and strength.

That's why the Rocky Mountain Cancer Rehabilitation Institute was established in 1996. Its founder got breast cancer and wondered if exercise could help alleviate some of the effects of chemo medications (increased resting heart rate, lowered RBC count, lowered WBC count, etc.). Quickly it was learned that exercise definitely helps, but the question has been, "At what intensity?" The answer is that there is no one answer. It varies from person to person.

RMCRI's mission is: *to relieve suffering, promote self-sufficiency, improve quality of life, and eliminate secondary cancers and cancer recurrence for cancer survivors through prescriptive exercise and evidence-based interventions.*

Today, my BMI, my maximum heart rate, and my resting heart rate (which is still a little on the high side due to chemo) were calculated. On the treadmill, I started off slowly with a walking pace. I was told that there are two ways of calculating the level of exertion: one is by using percentages of maximum heart rate and the other is to use RPE (rate of perceived exertion). My therapist uses a combination of the two so that patients can get a feel for how hard they're working alongside the actual heart rate numbers.

As I progressed from walking to running while she increased the speed and incline, she'd ask me to tell her my RPE and then

CANCER & Other Things I'm Grateful For

compare that to my heart rate to see how close I was. Turns out, I was always pretty close, even a little under, which she said she'd rather see that than someone who *thinks* they're working at a six when their heart rate is only at three.

I performed well on the treadmill test, able to go the entire twenty-one-minute duration. She said that most patients she sees last an average of seven to eight minutes on the treadmill. After I cooled down and we went back into her office, she compared my results to the normative data. For women aged forty to forty-nine who have had breast cancer, my VO_2 max was off that chart at 40.0. The highest level on the cancer patient scale stops at 25.0.

Then we looked at how I compare to the general population of forty- to forty-nine-year-old women. On that scale, I am at the penultimate level: excellent. That scale tops out at superior which is considered 45.0 and above.

She explained that the goal from here regarding my recovery is to maintain a steady linear improvement in fitness and not experience peaks and valleys regarding my fatigue over time. Therefore, my exercise prescription is to do three sessions per week of cardiovascular exercise of my choice working at a four to six RPE and 40–60 percent of my MHR sustained for twenty to thirty minutes for two months. She said that if in these next two months, I feel like I'm ready to progress before my retest, I can, but to increase only one variable at a time. Her suggestion was to keep the RPE and percentage of MHR the same but increase the duration to forty-five minutes.

She said that that doesn't mean I can't do other activities too, but that I should be raising my heart rate to this level only three times a week. The rest of the time, I can do gentle yoga, lift light weights, take leisurely walks or bike rides. But she said that I will see more significant gains if I don't overtax myself and take it slowly.

I was very excited to see that my metrics matched up with how I feel. I'm not usually a numbers girl, but for this purpose, I will wear a heart-rate monitor and keep close tabs on my exertion. I'll also start a fitness log so I can track accurately.

I will be grateful in perpetuity for how well my body has recovered from this and continues to recover. I am being mindful of what I'm asking my body to do. I am now fully aware of what it means to appreciate my health.

"Cultivating Happy Return"
September 9, 2015

Yesterday, while still in Ohio visiting my family, I went to yoga with Kerrianne at her regular studio. It was a hatha yoga class with an amazing instructor who talked about moving through postures slowly and, in between each side, not rushing the same set of movements—instead, going back to the center and doing whatever feels right for your body to balance before moving to the other side. He called it "cultivating happy return."

For me, it meant more than that in two other respects:

One is that I was returning home (I grew up in Ohio). And it was happy! Kerrianne had a wonderful party for me, and I got to spend time with lots of people I love. I hadn't seen everyone since I'd gone through cancer treatment, so I am grateful to get that chance.

The second is that during that class, I had a pose come back into my practice that I'd not been able to do since my surgery. Namely, eagle arms (arms are intertwined in front of your body and then bent toward the sky.) Since my surgery, it's been exceedingly difficult to do because of the lack of shoulder and scapular mobility.

The instructor walked us through a series of twists, focusing on scapular movement. Asking us to think about moving one scapula up and the other down. One forward and one toward the spine. After an hour, it was that isolation of movement that found me patiently following instructions and suddenly realizing, "I'm doing eagle arms!"

It was joyful.

Then Don't Worry

I ended up being quite late to PT today because traffic was quite thick and slow. Because I left my phone at home, I couldn't call, and I couldn't reroute. I just sat in my car, realizing that I, too, am traffic and there was literally nothing else I could do. I sang along to the radio as I remembered a yoga class where the instructor talked about when you have a problem and there's literally nothing you can do about it, then don't worry. So, I didn't. I was going to be twenty-five minutes late if I worried or not. And as it always does . . . life goes on.

"From Soup to Nuts"
September 14, 2015

My second surgery is now scheduled. It'll be Tuesday, January 19, 2016. The first surgery of the day and of the week for my doctor.

Today, I had my last tissue expansion, and now I don't have to see him until my pre-op appointment in January.

At my appointment today with his physician assistant, we talked all about that surgery: what my recovery time is likely to be, what my restrictions will be, and implant choices. I asked her if during surgery I'll be moved into a sitting position. I've been thinking about that a lot lately. How could he possibly tell how things look while I'm lying down? Turns out, they will sit me up. My arms will be attached to boards on either side and the table moves up into a nearly ninety-degree angle. That made me feel better. She said that the second surgery is an art form, much like a sculpture. She said that, lately, his results have been astoundingly good. I'm very excited for this surgery. To have it on the calendar is a gigantic relief. Additionally, having the tissue expansion complete is a big relief. That's been a long process that began in late May.

I enjoy checking things off the list. I have all of my remaining immunotherapy treatments on the calendar as well. I have five of those left, finishing on December 17.

True Religion

I don't consider myself a religious person, per se. But that doesn't mean that I'm not spiritual or don't believe in a higher power. I've had a lot of opportunities to think about faith during my illness. Mostly, I struggle with the labels and classifications assigned to religions. People have asked what denomination I am. I don't know how to even begin to answer that. I usually give the abridged version, "I grew up Catholic." But that says very little about my belief system now.

I don't like scare tactics. I don't like guilt. I don't like separation and labeling. I don't subscribe to one doctrine. I understand that people get a lot out of their particular brand of faith. But that doesn't mean that they have it figured out and everyone else is wrong.

I have been reading Wayne Dyer lately. He's a psychologist and author of twenty-plus books on self-empowerment. He talks a lot about understanding the definition of God and the many incarnations "he" takes in religion. For me, God isn't a person. For me, it's easier to think about God as the "universe."

Part of me hesitates to write all of what I really think about defined religion because I fear that I'll be judged, which in itself is not what religion should be about. I'm pretty sure that we were given minds to think and create and imagine and decide. It's not our place to judge others. And I'm not even sure that God judges us. That seems like a horrendous way to go through life: constantly being judged by your creator. I believe that we all do the best we can. And when we know better, we do better. And our creator, our source, our God, our universe knows that.

Secondhand Stress

This is something new I've been thinking about lately. As if we don't have enough of our own stress, we visit upon ourselves the stress of others. No matter who that might be, anyone from a boss to a store clerk. Lately, I'm realizing that I do it a lot. I feel like in order to empathize, I have to be equally frazzled, but that's not true.

My inner calm should be strong enough to hear about someone else's problem and not get stressed out. That's not to say that I won't help out if I can, but cooler heads are more effective than flying off the handle.

From now on, I am consciously *not* inhaling all the secondhand stress. I'm trying to stay focused in the bliss of my inner world. We'll see how that works out for me. Tough habit to break.

My Hair

In short, it's growing.

The longer story is that I'm using it as my guide to my overall recovery. My hair is an obvious reminder of what I've been through. I lost it all when I was at my sickest. And now it's coming back, just like the rest of my systems. I do have hair, but it's not quite like it was—just like my fitness, my neuropathy, my nails. But it's all coming back. I am thinking that just about the time that my hair is where I want it to be, everything else will have returned to normal as well.

"Everything Will Be Okay in the End"
September 25, 2015

The end is in sight; yesterday I finished my sixteenth immunotherapy infusion. Only four more to go. Until this point, it has seemed too soon to begin a countdown. But now, I have one in October, two in November, and one in December. I'll be done before Christmas.

Here's a quick reminder of the whole chemo plan: from December 2014 to April 2015, I was on four medications. All are designed to eliminate cancer, but different types and in different ways. Two immunotherapy medications were used to target my specific type of cancer (HER2+). After April, I continued getting infusions of one of them—twenty in all. That was always the plan from day one. It doesn't mean that I still have cancer.

In reality, there are two goals of cancer treatment: eradicating existing cancer and preventing recurrence. What I'm doing now is preventing recurrence. Radiation served the same purpose.

The immunotherapy medication doesn't make me sick. But it carries with it the risk of cardiotoxicity. In about 4 percent of patients, it can cause heart failure. Therefore, it's important for me to have an echocardiogram every three months. What they're measuring is known as ejection fraction, or what percentage of my blood volume is pumped out with every beat. It gives them an indicator of heart muscle strength. It is considered normal between 50 and 70 percent. Mine has been steady at 69 percent.

My oncologist said that most people who have an issue tend to have other comorbidities (e.g., diabetes, obesity, heart disease) so my risk is very low. To help maintain my heart health, I am still exercising nearly every day. I do a harder workout three times a week. And other days, I do a less intense activity. This keeps my heart muscle strong. I'm also careful to get plenty of sleep.

Butch has given me some other natural supplements to protect my heart as well: CoQ10, taurine, acetyl L-carnitine, and a high dose of vitamin E (an antioxidant). I'll stay on them till just before my surgery on January 19.

Pick Two

I was reading an article the other day and it said that Steven Spielberg had a sign on his door that said, "FAST, CHEAP, GOOD. PICK TWO."

I started thinking about that concept in terms of trade-offs we make all the time, particularly for our health. You can eat fast food; it's cheap and it's easy, but it's not good for you. Maybe the trade-off is an opportunity cost: you decide that sleeping in is more important than getting up for a Saturday morning bike ride. Often, we choose excuses over results.

"Do You Know Where You're Lucky?"
October 8, 2015

One of my favorite movies is *As Good As It Gets*, and one of my favorite scenes from that movie is toward the end when Melvin (Jack Nicholson) is in a complete panic about what to do about Carol (Helen Hunt). Then Simon (Greg Kinnear) asks Melvin quite plainly and with a bit of envy, "Do you know where you're lucky, Melvin?" Melvin gives him a blank look and a quick shake of his head. Simon explains, "You know who you *want*!"

On a regular basis, I ask myself this very question: "Do you know where you're lucky?" There's always something positive in every situation. I believe that in earnest.

Many people, myself included, wonder why I got cancer. I'm not sure I'll ever know why. I've lived a very active and healthy lifestyle. So much so that Kerrianne calls me "The Organic Squirrel."

And while I didn't *want* cancer, I'm glad to have had this experience. Thankful, even.

That may sound wacky to you. I can understand why. It's not like I'm saying I wish it upon myself, but once it was there, I was better off working with it and learning from it than pitching a fit about it. I've learned so much during this time. I often wonder if I would have ever learned these things without having gone through cancer.

I was scared, but not of dying. Mostly I was scared of the treatments. They were pretty brutal and life-changing. It's not like I refused to allow the possibility of death to enter my mind—it just didn't. I remember one of my doctors saying to me last December, "It's going to be a hard eighteen months." That was the single best thing he could've said to me because it showed that he wasn't giving up on me, delivering a death sentence. He was telling me that the next eighteen months of my life would be hard in order for me to have the next indeterminate number of years yet to live.

That's fine. Eighteen months is doable. It has sucked at times, being sick, being weak. But I knew where I was lucky.

I'm not naive. I know people die of cancer. I've had people very close to me die of cancer. I just felt confident that I would be healthy again one day. And I think that's monumentally important to healing. I'm not saying that's all it takes. But I am saying that a positive attitude goes a long way toward helping the body do its job. If the body and mind are at odds, that's counterproductive. During treatment, I would talk to my body to let it know that the treatment is meant to heal and would be a good thing in the long term.

I believe that we are presented with challenges in our lives, and until we learn the lessons they are trying to teach, they come back in new and different ways. I know now what I was to learn from cancer. The lessons are almost limitless. One of the most important lessons is that, now, I remember to ask, "Do you know where you're lucky?" And because I got what I needed, I can now say good-bye—and thank you—to cancer.

Gratitude, always.

Always, gratitude.

Is, Ys, and Ts

I had physical therapy. My therapist said that my muscles are becoming less tight and my range of motion is improving. I talked to her about some of my limitations in my arms and shoulders. She said that I have weaknesses more than range of motion issues because if someone moves my arm into place, it'll go. But when I try, I strain and contort and my shoulder blade pops up.

She gave me some new exercises to do on a physioball. I am to lie on my stomach and with my arms in front, form an *I* with my arms, and hold it for twenty to thirty seconds. Then move to a *Y* position, again holding. And finally, *T*. I am to do ten sets a day. Then flip over and do the same while on my back. The ones on my stomach will strengthen my scapulae. The ones on my back will stretch my chest.

I'm glad to have the option of reconstructive surgery, but to be frank, this part sucks. Kind of a lot. The expanders are solid, stationary, and immobile. They feel nothing like natural breasts and more like baseballs under my skin. By the time I get my expanders out, I will have had them in for nine months. My physical therapist tells me every week that I'll feel like a new person when I get my permanent implants.

This phase sucks for reasons I didn't know it would. I have a lot of neck and shoulder pain because my arms can't rest in a natural position. They're always either forward or behind the expanders, which are immobile, by design.

For now, all I can do is exercises to make this process more comfortable and be grateful that this, too, shall pass. I keep thinking that this stage will make me even more grateful for the beautifully rendered finished product. But January 19 can't come soon enough.

"Three Treatments Left"
October 15, 2015

After today's treatment, I have two treatments in November and one in December which will round out my year of chemotherapy/immunotherapy. It wasn't how I envisioned spending 2015 but that's certainly how it worked out. From a spiritual perspective, it may not have been what I *wanted* but it was certainly what I *needed*.

When I saw my oncologist today, he complimented my hair and asked me more questions about it than anything else. So that gives you an idea of how smoothly things are going right now. We chatted about hair and fingernails, and his spiffy new cowboy boots.

After that, my echocardiogram was uninspiring. The technician was nice enough. But I wanted to grab a stethoscope and listen for *his* heartbeat. He didn't smile or change the tone of his voice. Or even look at me, now that I think about it. He did apologize for how hard he had to press the transducer into my chest. So that was nice.

I'll get the results in about a week. So far, it's been in the normal range (between fifty and seventy). Fingers crossed.

"Trust Your Gut"
October 15, 2015

Today, I went through my German notebook that I used when I was taking lessons. Near the back was a page of notes written in pink ink. It was from the day I met with the medical team of oncologists at a university hospital last December. I went alone to my appointments on this day because Michael had to travel for work. So, I wanted to take notes to be sure I could relay all the information. I had written each doctor's name and specialty at the top of each section.

As I read it today, I remembered how I felt the day I met with them. There were four doctors: a medical oncologist, a surgical oncologist, a plastic surgeon, and a radiation oncologist. They came in one at a time in succession and gave me the rundown on my situation. They were cold, clinical. They were scary. They were pushy. They tried to impress me with the statistics on how many patients they've treated, how big the hospital is, what resources they have. They tried to convince me to do a clinical trial. I felt like they were simply happy that they had a candidate for their HER2+ trial.

I left there feeling like I had escaped.

At the time, I had mixed feelings about choosing that hospital for my care. On the one hand, it was a preselected team that would coordinate my care. They'd meet about my treatment on a regular basis. The right hand would know what the left hand was up to. I wouldn't have to assemble a team piecemeal; I was given the full complement. But I just couldn't shake the feeling that I didn't *like* any of them. Not one of them asked me anything about me. It was like an assembly line. My gut was telling me that I wouldn't be happy with them.

I left there in a hurry because I had an appointment with a different surgical oncologist. When I got to her office, I was feeling so overwhelmed. I wasn't sure I could take in any more information. Then she came in. The first thing she said was, "This is a tough time. You look tired. What can I tell you that you haven't already heard? I want to be helpful and not overwhelm you."

I was sold.

I'm eternally glad I made the decision not only to have her as my surgeon but that I would build my team around her at that hospital. Within the next week, I'd made the choices for the rest of my team. I did all of this with little guidance. I was flying blind and, somehow, I ended up with the best team of doctors that can be assembled in Denver. And that's not just my opinion. It's the opinion of many dozens of doctors, nurses, technicians, patients, and physical therapists that ask who my doctors are. They just smile, nod, and say, "Wow, you've got the best!" And I know it's true.

My surgical oncologist isn't just any surgeon, she's *the* surgeon who has developed advanced techniques for better outcomes for mastectomy patients. Why? Not because it makes her job easier but because it leaves minimal scarring and a better overall outcome for the patients. It turns out that my reconstructive surgeon isn't just the superhero of breast reconstruction, he's also a volunteer surgeon for cleft-palate surgery organizations in third-world countries. My oncologist isn't just an oncologist, he's one of the best in the country, and people come from all over to be treated by him. My radiation oncologist isn't just a radiation oncologist, he's a man who brings in massage therapists and acupuncturists and nutritionists to help care for his patients' total health and well-being at no charge to the patients. Literally, free massage. Weekly. I wasn't even allowed to tip. Heaven.

My surgical oncologist's name was given to me by the radiologist who performed my mammograms, ultrasounds, MRIs, and biopsies to get my diagnosis. I was given three names by her. She said that the first doctor on the list would be hard to get into. It was true. I was diagnosed on December 3. I got into my surgeon on December 9. (In the cancer world, that's an eternity. Other doctors saw me the next day.) But she's so busy because she's so *good*! Worth waiting for. Wow. Now, there's an understatement.

Last week I was a patient model for the oncology rehab group; the physical therapy students in class all remarked that my surgeon had done a wonderful job. Early on in this process, I wouldn't have known what that meant. But I can now understand and appreciate what a "good" mastectomy is.

I'm glad that despite the confusion, fear, and complete overwhelm I was feeling while planning my treatment, I was able to listen to my gut. It's not always easy to do. But it has rarely steered me wrong. In this case, it was spot on.

"FEAR: I Have a Choice in How I Deal with It"
October 26, 2015

I met someone today who had breast cancer too. As she told me her story, she didn't smile once. She's about my age, and a lot further along in her process than I. She's more than a year post-treatment. Though I don't know her at all, she seemed kind. As we talked, I kept thinking she looked scared and sad.

It made me think about my situation. I smile a lot; I am happy for many things. Even to tell my cancer story, I'm happy about many aspects: I'm happy I found it in time. I'm happy that effective chemo was available. I'm happy I had a complete pathological response. I'm happy that radiation is over. I'm happy that my range of motion is returning. I'm happy that I have an amazing medical team. I'm happy that I'm feeling good. I'm happy that I can exercise again. I am happy that I'm healthy.

I suppose I could be sad that it happened at all, but that's just not me. I don't sit around thinking of myself as a fighter or that I'm going to kick cancer's ass. That implies anger. And I'm just not angry.

I am resourceful. I am resilient. I am creative. I am positive. I am persistent.

Everyone handles their situations differently. But this is one thing I know for sure: I have a choice in how I feel about it.

Don't get me wrong. This is no walk in the park. Many things about it suck. Every step has been difficult in its own way. Difficult *and* successful. Just because it was difficult doesn't mean I am resentful or worn down. And just because it was successful doesn't mean I'm not ready to kiss it good-bye.

I think the most difficult thing about cancer is that it's a long process. It doesn't end when chemo does, or when surgery is over, or after six weeks of daily radiation. It's a process that takes as long as it takes. By that, I mean that there's a lot of medical treatments, over which I had little to no control of the timing and effects. But there's also mental stuff and spiritual stuff and unless I deal with that in a constructive and immediate way, it will last forever. And that's why I am trying to deal with it all in a constructive and immediate way. I've been proactive.

I want to return to normal life. Does that mean I will forget this experience and never look back? No. It means that life didn't end when I was told that I had cancer. I did have to take a pause from my normal routine to go through it, but now I'm ready to resume my life. Yes, cancer changed me but that doesn't mean it made me worse, less healthy, or scarred. It made me ever more grateful. It made me better able to live in the present. It made me more empathetic. It made me less inhibited. It made me care even less about what people think of me.

I feel like a lot of people live in fear. I learned a while back that fear stands for "False Expectations Appearing Real." And if I sit around worrying about cancer returning, then I'm more likely to bring that into my life than if I go about living life to the fullest. Worrying is nothing but praying for a bad outcome. What we think about we bring about. I know this for sure.

"Hail Butch"
November 17, 2015

Today I had acupuncture with Butch, and I talked to him about my tight shoulder muscles. Because I had radiation on my left upper back, the muscles along my shoulder and neck are very tight. I've had a knot in my upper trapezius for a couple of months. When I go to physical therapy, she works on it very thoroughly and it feels better, but temporarily.

I mentioned this to Butch, and he said he had some things he could do. During acupuncture, he focused on the point in my foot that is connected to that shoulder energy. Then when I was done with my session, he had me roll onto my side and did dry needling in that muscle.

I've heard bad things about dry needling, mostly that it hurts. But it didn't. In fact, I felt release in that moment. He hit four spots that had been hurting the most. And then he stuck a magnet with a small needle in the center of that muscle to help it continue to release. I'm supposed to leave the magnet on for two to three days at a time. He gave me a packet of eight magnets. So far, it feels great. Tomorrow morning, I have physical therapy that should further help.

"The Days Were Long"
December 2, 2015

Tomorrow marks the day in 2014 when I was first told that I had breast cancer.

I would say that it's the day I found out, but I already knew. I remember the first time it actually occurred to me that it was cancer. I was in the office of the technician who performed my thermogram. Before we reviewed my images, she explained to me through the use of other peoples' anonymous images what to look for: how blood supply should appear in healthy breasts and how it looks when a tumor is present.

Then she brought my images up on the screen. And there it was—to me, irrefutable evidence that I had cancer. There was a hyper-red area with lots and lots of blood supply going to it. Cancer is a very smart thing. It knows how to skirt the system and get its own life support. I sat there staring at the screen, thinking, *Wow. I actually do have cancer.*

That's not what the technician said, of course. She simply said that it was necessary for me to have further testing. The weeks that followed until December 3 were excruciating for me.

In that time, I had an ultrasound, a mammogram, a biopsy, and an MRI. All this to tell me what I already knew. So, when I got the call one year ago, I was not surprised. I was just ready to get moving with treatment. Once the diagnosis was made, I was ready to hit the ground running. I had doctors' names lined up, waiting to do something.

I wanted to start treatment. After all, I'd just found out that I had stage III locally advanced invasive ductal carcinoma. At the same time, I wanted to do it right. I worked tirelessly to figure out how to do all that. Then I just had to sit back and hope it was right.

When I look back over this last year, it has felt like it has both zoomed by and dragged on. I think it's a lot like parenthood: the days are long; the years are short.

I was chatting with my physical therapist recently about approaching the one-year mark. She said that the next year will be filled with those milestones. It's an important year. It's necessary to look back to see how far I've come. And be grateful.

Always grateful. Grateful always.

Back into Physical Fitness

Yesterday, I did Tabata drills for my workout. These are high-intensity intervals. It's only twenty-one minutes. But it's the hardest twenty-one minutes I could imagine. For me, it's perfect. It gets my heart rate high and lets it briefly recover before bringing it right back up. This is the way to increase VO₂ max. It was really hard. It's the first time I've done Tabatas in more than a year. But I am excited to see how I improve over these next several weeks.

We've had too much snow to bike. And it's been super cold recently. I'm sure we'll get warm days again soon, but the ice on the ground is a big deterrent.

"Hello from the Other Side"
December 11, 2015

As I look at my posts from last December, I feel such tenderness for the "me" that I was. I had no idea what lay ahead of me. I knew the words "chemotherapy," "mastectomy," and "radiation." But what I didn't know was all the things that each entailed and what it would all mean to me.

I have said countless times in this process, "Well, no one told me about that!" I could give you examples, but I don't remember them, and I certainly don't want to be guilty of fear-mongering. Unfortunately, everyone has to have their own experience with cancer because no two people are alike.

So I will say this: I'm proud of me. When I look back on what my body, mind, and soul went through this year, I am amazed at the sheer amount of trauma I endured and was able to persevere. Before I had cancer, I thought that having cancer affected the body in a whole different way. The truth is, I didn't know how much of the body it does affect. The answer is the entire body. I mean that in the literal sense. From the top of my head to the tips of my toes. In fact, I still get nerve pain in the tips of my toes and my hair is still growing back.

To be honest, it's a solitary process. As much as I had people around me to care for me and help me, no one can really understand unless/until it's you. And even then, everyone's situation is different.

It's scary to be as debilitated as I have been. I'm regaining all of my faculties. But it has not been easy. And it's likely to take me a couple of years to be at full capacity. That's okay. I'm glad to be given the opportunity to heal and persist.

Just keep this in mind when you're dealing with a family member, friend, or coworker who has had cancer. Just because the treatments are over, or the surgery is complete, doesn't mean that everything is "back to normal."

There is no "back." There's just a new normal.

Chapter Twelve

Reconstruction

"Surgery Month!"
January 2, 2016

I can hardly believe that January is finally here. I'm seventeen days away from my surgery. Next Thursday, I have my pre-op appointment with my reconstructive surgeon, and I'll have blood work done after that.

This past week, I had two appointments with Butch: one to discuss my upcoming surgery and make a plan for my supplements, the other for acupuncture.

He has me taking a regimen of high-dose vitamins, minerals, and herbs for fourteen days, then stopping them for five days prior to my surgery. The point is to nourish my body with supplements to aid in tissue healing and scar prevention as well as boost immunity. The list of things I'm taking is long and varied. Some things are once a day, some are twice, and some are three times. Some things are best at night. Some are best in the morning. To avoid confusion, I made a spreadsheet that's hanging on my fridge. It was way easier to think it through once, design a table, and just check them off as I go.

I'll see Butch once more before my surgery for acupuncture.

And I'll see Sally once before then too. She helped me immensely last time by teaching me about guided imagery. I will be using the same CD as I did last time.

Also, next Thursday, I have my final echocardiogram to make sure my heart handled the immunotherapy treatments well.

My surgery is on Tuesday, January 19, at eight a.m. It is outpatient, as long as I tolerate the anesthesia well. I'm told that I'll be less sedated this time than last. Thank goodness. I spent six and a half hours in PACU last time. If that happens again, they'll keep me overnight.

Please send your positive energy, good vibes, and prayers my way for a quick post-anesthesia recovery.

"New Year, New Boobs"
January 7, 2016

Today, I ordered my new boobs. Turns out that it's a lot like bathing suit shopping. My plastic surgeon and I looked at a variety of implant styles and sizes. We decided on two styles in a variety of sizes. He'll try them all on me during surgery. I'll keep the ones I want, send back the rest!

The difference is that the surgeon will be making my decision for me. We talked about the pros and cons of the two styles. It comes down to what looks best. I'll be out, so it'll be up to him and his surgical assistant to make the call. We talked about what I'm looking for in an end result and what my lifestyle is like. I am in good hands. Literally.

He will sit me up during surgery to make sure they're even and look right. This stage is a lot like a sculpture. I've seen his work and I know he'll do a great job.

I'm so excited for this step. The only part that doesn't thrill me is the anesthesia. I get pretty sick from it. So today I requested my anesthesiologist. I want the one that I had for my port implant. I'm not sure that he'll be any better/different from the last one, but I liked him. That counts for a lot. My surgeon obliged. He asked his nurse to place the request. There's no guarantee that I'll get him, but it's a start.

I Got My Hair Did

I got my hair styled. I would say "cut" but that's only true on the neckline. I had to get that part tidied up, but the front has a lot of growing to do to catch up so we're leaving that alone. We played around with the styling and came up with a new look now that the sides are long enough to tuck behind my ears. I like it. It's still very limiting. But in order to keep my sanity, I'm going back to get it colored this weekend. I'm no fan of the darkness. Color choice is the part that is fun to me!

"A Journey of the Soul"
February 2, 2016

Earlier today, I thought about writing a blog post and then wondered what I'd write about. After all, my second surgery was textbook. I feel great, blah, blah, blah. Why bother? Not too much to say. And then I felt a little universal smack upside the head with a voice inside that said: That's exactly why you *should* write! Because you have a lot to be thankful for. Voice it! Gratitude, always. Always, gratitude.

My second surgery was two weeks ago today and it went off without a hitch. As always, my surgeon and his team under-promised and overdelivered. I am thrilled with the results.

My anesthesiologist was likewise amazing. I had zero nausea. I was awake and aware within ten minutes in the PACU. I felt fine, perfectly fine. My throat was a little scratchy from the tube, but I got some ice cubes then some apple juice.

I talked to my surgeon in the PACU. He's the first person I saw. My first question? "What size am I?" Let's just say I'm proportionate and happy with that too.

Within about two and a half hours, I was changed, home, and ready for a big ol' bowl of noodles. I made it clear to everyone at the hospital that I was displeased with the fasting rule. I honestly believe that at least half the reason that I feel so sick after anesthesia is because they don't let me eat. Who can take all that medication on an empty stomach and feel fine? Not me. Evidently, there are some procedures and some anesthesiologists who will allow a modified fasting plan. I will check into that, if needed in the future.

All around, the experience was textbook. There's a lot to be said for textbook. It means it was done as well as they strive to teach every reconstructive surgeon to do it. That's saying something.

I feel there is no adequate way to thank my doctors and their staff. I will try my best by telling others how wonderful, amazing, unbelievable, and caring they are so that others can have as good an experience as I've had.

Post-Op

In these two weeks since surgery, I've healed fast. But I started from a vastly different place compared to the mastectomy. There really is no way to fairly compare the first surgery with the second.

Before the second surgery, I was chemo free, had been doing yoga daily, had a VO$_2$ max of 40.0, and had regained most of my weight, strength, and range of motion. Plus, the extent of the involvement of muscles and tissues in the second surgery is a small fraction compared to the first.

In the second surgery, there was simply removing the temporary expanders and putting in the permanent implants. Easy peasy!

Sort of.

That's the basic concept, of course, but for my surgeon, it's never a cakewalk. He takes his time, he's serious, caring, and a perfectionist. He tried all sorts of sizes and types till he got the look he was going for. He had some extra work to do on my radiated side because the tissue is a bit damaged, so he needed to open up some pockets and get everything even. There was also lots of work to do along my sternum to get a nice close spacing in the center. He's a master.

I've had two follow-up appointments since surgery. At the first one, they let me take off the gigantic, corset-like, ill-fitting, surgical bra and let me start wearing a soft, stretchy, front-closure sports bra. Big improvement. I was also taught how to begin self-massage to keep the implants mobile, the skin lax, and generally, everything going in the correct direction (not too far north or south).

Yesterday was my second follow-up appointment. They removed the adhesive bandages and showed me how to place the silicon strips along the incisions to begin scar healing. I'd like to explain how thin these incisions are. Take out a piece of lined notebook paper. Look closely at a single printed line in the middle of the page. And then block off a two-inch section with your fingers. That's it! I was so happy to see that, and I'm determined to keep them thin and light till they fade away.

In addition to the silicon strips I wear during the day (think teeth-whitening strips, only stickier), every night I remove the strips then massage the incisions with a silica-based oil. And as I always do, I have some other tricks of the trade that I'm doing: I take turmeric, silica, and vitamin E orally. The turmeric is supposed to be fantastic, but only when taken with black pepper for absorption. I'm taking a brand I found at my local health food store, and it contains black pepper. Then the silica and vitamin E are from Butch.

At this point, I'm allowed to use any product on my skin that I know won't irritate me. So, I'll bust out the products I used during radiation that did such a fantastic job: emu oil, tamanu oil, and calendula oil.

No Regrets

For these past fourteen months, it feels like I've been on a long journey and yet, I've gone nowhere. At least not anywhere physically. But I've been just about everywhere in my soul. Throughout this time, I've had jaw-dropping epiphanies, mind-blowing experiences, and soul-crushing disappointments.

Sally and I have talked a lot about what I am to learn from having had cancer. I don't know that I've learned everything I am to learn, but I have learned a lot so far.

Some things I've learned are these:

- Own my shit: be aware enough to recognize and claim my flaws, problems, issues, but don't make them anyone else's responsibility. The flip side: do not take on others' shit. That is theirs alone to figure out.

- Be content with what is: be at peace with whatever I have to deal with. It means to be content with what I have. And I have a lot: free will, gumption, and chutzpah, resources (financial, human, and emotional) to do something about it. Whatever "it" is.
- Look inside and be unafraid: to be contemplative, content, and yet always willing to expand and grow. That's what it's all about. It's not about what you look at, it's what you see.
- Be grateful: Once I read something that said, "Imagine that if you woke up tomorrow and everything you hadn't expressed gratitude for were gone." I suddenly found myself thankful for everything from my family and friends to my washing machine and butter.
- No regrets: Do more things today that my future self will thank me for.
- Empathy: Just because some people's issues are out there for everyone to see doesn't mean that we don't all have our issues. So never judge people if you know the whole story or not. Everyone handles things in different ways, and we are all doing our best, even if our best looks bad to others. Some people out there who are struggling have had plenty of opportunities to do good in their lives and have squandered it. Others have faced such seemingly insurmountable obstacles that it's a wonder they get out of bed every day. Other people imagine their obstacles.

I've been going through a lot of stuff over these fourteen months. And it was a bit overwhelming at times. But I managed, with self-reliance, help from others, and a competent medical team. At my last appointment with Sally, she asked me if I'd change anything about my treatment, my doctors, or my decisions. The answer is no.

That feels so deeply satisfying, I feel it in my bones.

There's no way out, just through.

"*Parla Come Mangi*"
February 3, 2016

There's one thing I forgot to mention about what I've learned during cancer treatment: be true to my Self.

Throughout my life, I've had people tell me things like, "Tone it down," or "Dial it back." I wondered, "What's 'it'?" and "There's a dial?"

I've come to realize this about my Self: I'm an enthusiastic person. When I like something, I express it clearly. When I find something funny, I laugh, genuinely.

I love to sing. I'm not skilled, but I enjoy it. I've been told that what I lack in skill, I make up for in volume and enthusiasm.

I have high highs and low lows. I don't have bipolar disorder nor am I an imbecile. I just react to things that happen to me *when* they happen to me and according to *how I feel* about them. I've come to realize that that's how I want to live—and there are some people who don't. They're reserved. They have poker faces, whereas I have a miniature golf face (thanks to Liz Gilbert for helping me name it).

At times, my kids get a little embarrassed that I laugh "too" loud at the movies or when something tickles me in public. "Here she goes," they say. Know what? If the thing they say about their mom that embarrasses them is that she laughs too much, then life's good.

I have an earthy sense of humor. It's difficult to offend me. Therefore, I find some jokes/things funny that others would be embarrassed by or find off-putting. For better or worse, I've passed this on to my kids. We have a rule in our house that what's said at the dinner table isn't repeated. Not everyone can handle our candor.

Also, I have a quality about myself wherein I tell it like it is. That doesn't mean I go around telling people off. But I am open to telling the unobstructed truth: "That is not what we agreed to." "That won't work for me." As an adult, I've learned how to do this calmly and firmly. Parenthood helped. I've stopped qualifying my statements, "Honestly . . ." or "If you want the truth . . ." And

I just say the thing! Spit it out! As the Italians say, *"Parla come mangi!"* It's an idiom that means, "Speak like you eat!"

A small part of me still sometimes wonders if I should quietly acquiesce. I wonder about this less as I become more and more able to be true to my Self. An artificial way of life doesn't work for me. I have no veneer.

The last part of being true to my Self that I've discovered is that I'm the ultimate secret keeper. Remember the vault from *Seinfeld*? I've got a big vault. I don't gossip or tell tales to gain acceptance. I have learned whom in my life I can trust with things and whom I can't. I value this undisputedly above all else. I think I'm a fairly open book about my life, but when it comes to things that are sacred to me and I want them held in high regard, I'm careful about whom I trust. I am someone whom others can trust with their treasured thoughts, ideas, memories, and insecurities as well.

It's taken me forty-four years, eight months, and two days to learn that not everyone will like me. That's okay. That's about them; it's not that I'm lacking something likable. I don't feel that everyone "should" like me, and if they don't then they're missing something. But I have learned that most times when people don't like something about another person it's because they either see or *don't* see the same trait in themselves that they either wish they had or wish they didn't.

Jealousy sucks. Nowadays, when I find my Self feeling envious of someone's accomplishments or possessions, I turn that around to first feel happy for that person. Then second, I use their good fortune to inspire me. Sometimes, I can literally feel my Self filling up with the urge to do/learn/be/immerse my Self in something creative. Not because I'm trying to outdo anyone. But because I want to realize my own potential and knock my own socks off.

There have been times in my life when I thought that people cared about what I'm doing, what I have, what I think. I've come to realize that no one is paying attention to me at all. We're all busy having our own experiences.

Chapter Thirteen

Recovery

"Just Breathe"
February 11, 2016

I 've been a fan of the band Pearl Jam since the dawn of . . . well, Pearl Jam! The early '90s was when I started listening to them and, for me, they stood out from the rest of the Seattle grunge-band genre because of their lyrics. One song in particular: "Just Breathe."

Lately, I've been dealing with cancer, a cross-country move, job changes, two teenagers, college decisions, and all the rest of my daily life. So from time to time, I have a touch of stress.

I make a point of reducing all the unnecessary stressors that I can: drama queens and kings, complainers, the media circus, reality TV, crazy drivers, and material possessions.

But when I must be faced with a difficult situation, I remind myself that all I have to do is breathe. Literally.

Yoga has helped me immensely in remembering how to breathe. When we get excited, our breath quickens. It happens when we get mad. Sometimes when we hear terrible news, we hold our breath.

Whenever my kids come to me and they are upset (mostly when they were younger, but still occasionally), the first thing I say is,

"Take a deep breath. Again. Relax your shoulders. Now tell me." Repeat as necessary.

I think sometimes we take breathing for granted. Or maybe some of us think telling someone to breathe is trite. But breath is the life-giving force, prana. At birth, we bring the life force in. It's the first thing we do on this planet: inhale. And when we die, we let it go. It will be the last thing we do on earth: exhale. In between, all we must do is breathe.

Most of the time, we don't think about it. It just happens for us! And that's great, like a heartbeat. The difference is that we can choose to control it. We can breathe in and out on command. We can hold our breath. We can use breathing techniques. We can use our breath to express our words, our despair, and our gratitude.

But most of the time, we pay no attention to our breathing. Until it stops.

Recently, after my mastectomy, I had a hard time coming out of the anesthesia. I wasn't breathing well on my own. Even once my family was allowed back to see me, the nurse asked them to re-mind me to breathe. I was having about four rounds of breath per minute. During surgery, a machine breathes for you. It's important for life function to breathe, but it's also vital for our mental health.

Vital.

I keep a little rock on my desk as a reminder. Inhale the peace. Exhale the stress. Let it go.

"Slow Down"
February 13, 2016

I have always been careful about what I eat. I got cancer any-way. I don't know why, but I believe that it's the toxic load that I've been exposed to for forty-three years. One factor is that I grew up in the Ohio River Valley which is known for trapping toxic air. The cancer rates in that area of the country have been under in-vestigation for decades. I stopped living there when I was eighteen but the toxicity can remain with you for a long time.

It makes me sad that as a population, we're polluting ourselves to death: Eating too much of the wrong stuff. Leading sedentary lives. Developing new syndromes because of all the electronics we use.

I've always been a late adopter of technology. I still like using a pencil and paper calendar for my appointments. I like reading bona fide books. I liked when we put our memories in photo albums.

It's not that I'm a Luddite, I just like simple things. I like to slow down, take my time. Sure, the web is great, but I miss going to the Carnegie Public Library to do research by using the card catalog and finding books to read on wooden tables with glass tops. I liked being part of the summer reading contest when I had to fill out the card in the front pocket of each book with my name on it, and I could see everyone who had it before I. There's a quaintness there that I miss.

I think I must be an old soul.

Everything is so fast these days: internet speeds, information distribution, the pace of life.

In 2002, just weeks before she died of pancreatic cancer, my mother-in-law gave me a piece of advice that has stuck with me.

One weekend, we were wrapping up a visit to her and I was rushing around trying to get things together for our two-and-a-half-hour drive back home. The kids were little (four and one) and I felt like I was herding cats. Finally, we got the kids in the car and were ready to go. She stood in the sliding-glass doorway, and I said good-bye and gave her a hug. She said, "Slow down, and think about what you're doing."

That was the last time I saw her conscious and the last words she ever spoke to me.

So, I'll pass that advice on to the world: slow down, and think about what you're doing.

"Let It Go!"
February 17, 2016

Lately, I've been thinking about the idea of nonattachment, one of the eight limbs of yoga. It's in my nature to attach to things and ideas: outcomes, opportunities, possessions, abilities. I'm focusing my energy on letting go and am practicing *aparigraha*, the Sanskrit word for nonattachment.

I think that the phrase "let it go" can become misconstrued. It means to release yourself from the strain of feeling like you have control over things, which you do not. What it does not mean is to simply forget about it, bury it, deny it, stress over it, or hope so deeply that you miss out on the joy of the present. My therapist and I often talk about this concept in terms of trying to grasp a fistful of water. It's not possible. Only once you open up your hands and accept being a vessel can you hold what's intended for you.

That means I'm letting go of the stranglehold I have on things, so badly wanting things to go my way. Instead, I'm trying to do my best to be open to what life has to offer, and then letting go of the outcome.

It's freeing to do that. Otherwise, you become a slave to things which are utterly out of your control.

"Lace up Your Boots"
February 26, 2016

Sometimes I have these really calming experiences when I think that nothing could ever shake my innermost calm. I'm feeling perfectly zen. Utterly serene. Centered. Relaxed. Happy.

But then something pops up—a call from the school, I accidentally break a piece of antique china from Michael's grandmother, the pilot light goes out on the brand-new fireplace, I stub my third toe. And suddenly, I feel it boiling up inside me and I want to scream, "SONOFABITCH!"

Where did all that calmness go? I've been trying so hard to be grounded, breathe through the difficult stuff. And with just a few simple life moments, I feel like I'm back to square one. All that spiritual and mental work I've been doing is down the drain! Out comes the flurry of expletives. And I've completely lost my cool.

But guess what?

No amount of spiritual energy is ever wasted. Ever. It is always a noble, worthy, and deserving intention to raise your consciousness and be a person who exudes love, understanding, and acceptance.

I'm human. I slip up. The key is that once I do, I forgive myself and remain true to my intentions. I'm not perfect. News flash: no one is. Even those people who seem to float through life on a blessed cloud of bliss.

Exhibit A:

Last week, I was leaving yoga at oncology rehab. On my way out, two patients started talking to me about cancer stuff. Normally, I go to yoga to let go of cancer stuff, but I got sort of stuck, and I found myself unable to extricate myself. One woman was complaining about the reconstruction process, and she said that we've all had our hard times of dealing with it. And then she pointed at me and said, "Except maybe you. You always have that smile plastered on your face."

Whiskey Tango Foxtrot?

This was one of those times where I nearly lost my cool. I was feeling really good about the yoga class we'd just finished—physically, mentally, spiritually. And then this lady comes out of nowhere with an assumption that I never have hard times and that my smile is in some way not genuine. The old me would've said something snarky back. I even found myself trying to search for evidence that I've had hard times.

But then I realized something.

That comment was all about *her.* What she said is true: I come to yoga smiling and leave yoga smiling. Why? Because I'm freaking happy! Genuinely happy. I could list "reasons" why. But is that really necessary? It seems weird to have to justify why I'm happy. Because I am, damn it!

So, if this lady is looking for something to judge about me and the worst she can come up with is that I'm always smiling—well, it seems that that is her issue and not mine.

I'm going to continue smiling. I'm grateful for everything I have and am and do, even if I get a little sideways sometimes. Things happen. But as it always has, life goes on.

I figured out a way to avoid the cancer-complaint group after yoga. I simply take off my shoes and socks in a different area from everyone else. That way, at the end of class, I can quietly go to my corner, put them on, and walk out. As I pass by the group, I smile, wave, and say, "Have a nice night, ladies!"

Exhibit B:

On Wednesday, I was a patient model at a local university where my physical therapist teaches students pursuing their doctorate in PT. One part of the three-hour lab was to do a patient history and ask me questions about my experience from diagnosis till now. One student asked me how the process has affected me psychologically.

I told her that when I first discovered the lump, I knew in my gut it wasn't right. I just wanted an answer—which took nearly six weeks! Then I was busy finding my medical team. Once chemo started, I had all the time in the world to ponder all the questions that probably most cancer patients ponder.

I described my overriding attitude to the students like this: If it snows in May, you can sit inside wondering why or complaining about it or even being mad. *Or* you can lace up your boots and move on with life. I chose the latter.

I explained that my chemo worked amazingly well, and I had a complete pathological response to it. My medical team is amazing. I have wonderful family and friends to support me. So, I have a lot to be grateful for.

I added that there's a lot that I have done and continue to do for *myself*: I write a blog, I see a mental therapist, I see a physical therapist, I get acupuncture, I take Chinese herbs, I practice yoga on and off the mat, I meditate, I read, and I practice gratitude.

My wellness is up to *me*. I feel that this statement is requisite knowledge for these students to have (but really for everyone to have.) Yes, I need medical care to do the physical part. But my wellness and the active role I play in healing my body, mind, and spirit is up to me and no one else.

I laced up my boots.

"Time Marches On"
March 2, 2016

This evening I decided to go back and read my posts from last March. Man, a lot has happened in that year. Again, it's almost spring and we'll be gaining daylight.

My overriding feeling as I read the posts is to be thankful. Treatment was not easy. Last March, I was doing the one-month countdown to finishing chemo. It was tough, but it was effective. Highly effective. I feel well, and I'm happy.

Sometimes I feel like there should be someone to thank for my health. I don't really believe in a deity that is a human-like man. Instead, I think that there is a higher power, a universal force at work. Somehow, saying thank-you seems insufficient and even inappropriate. The universe doesn't want my thanks. I think I'm supposed to take my gratitude and do something with it—be a person who realizes her purpose, who is generous, and who creates a life of meaning for myself and others.

Since beginning my cancer recovery, one of the joys that has returned is the joy of eating. For a long time, my food tasted like metal, so I didn't feel like eating. But once it didn't anymore, all I wanted to do was eat. I had a deficit of about ten-plus pounds. Let's just say I've made up for that! Part of me knows that I can't just eat and gain nonstop. But there's part of me that's enjoying nourishing my body. I don't eat junk. But I have been having cream on my strawberries and 2-percent milk in my lattes and buttermilk fried chicken with crispy brussels sprouts. And the list goes on. I think it's what I need right now.

Today, I went back to my precancer yoga class. The classes are more physically demanding than the ones I do at oncology rehab. And I love them. It felt great to be back on my mat in that room. It's like home.

Tomorrow, I have an ultrasound to figure out the source of some bruising I've been dealing with. My reconstructive surgeon thinks it's not a major problem, but he wants to rule out a hematoma. Please wish me luck with that. I'm expecting that they will say that the source of the bruising is simply some trauma to the tissues during surgery. It's mostly gone now, but a little precaution is wise.

After the ultrasound, I'll go to PT. I've increased my sessions to two per week. I do a lot of rehab work here at home daily, but my therapist's techniques are like no other.

Butch gave me a homeopathic topical medication that alleviates inflammation symptoms to use on the sore and bruised tissue. It really helps, especially at night. These days, it feels pretty good to sleep on my side.

"Just 'Cause"
April 21, 2016

There's a musical artist named Vance Joy that I enjoy a lot. Every one of his songs has been a hit with me. Today while listening to the radio, the local DJ was talking about Vance being in town to perform a "Garage Session" and how he had previously been a lawyer who passed the bar, then a professional soccer player, and now a musician of world renown.

I knew I liked this guy. Not because he's famous but because he's following his heart. I'm guessing that people might've given him flak for leaving a stable career to play professional soccer. And then probably raised eyebrows again when he decided to launch a music career. But I love it!

That's what life is for. It's to figure out what makes you happy. And maybe many things make you happy. So go—try them *all!* Be a professional soccer-playing, singing lawyer. Whatever floats your boat.

I think that there's an antiquated thought that life isn't meant to be all fun and games. It's serious business. Responsibility. Duty.

I call bullshit.

Is there a time to be serious and responsible? Of course. But what we really need in this world is more people who are happy. Happiness is contagious. Happiness spreads like water under a door. It gets into all those little places you didn't even know it could go. And in turn, it makes more happy people. And so on and so on.

I applaud and admire creating a life of following your passion. To give up decades of work, education, and effort in one field to pursue something that is risky but fun, uncertain but fulfilling, difficult but rewarding shows a lot of character and chutzpah.

I'm not saying that you can't be happy on a traditional career path or in the same job for many years. Many people are quite happy and fulfilled. Sadly, many people are not. It's about what makes *you* happy. Not what pleases your parents, your spouse, or even your own ideas about doing what's expected.

It's okay to leave a stable and completely uninteresting job in order to try something new, then to realize it's not what you thought it would be. Go do something else!

There's no wasted time and effort in finding your bliss.

To me, it's obvious when I'm talking with someone who is passionate about what they are doing. I've had people say to me, "I go to work, and I go home. That's my life." *Wow.* I get it. We all need to work. But not all day, every day. Where does happiness come in? Where is the joy?

Do something that makes your soul sing even if it isn't what you do for your job. I read something recently that said, "Write down all the things you do in a day that make you happy. Do more of that."

Something I learned during cancer treatment is that I had to decide to be happy for no reason whatsoever. Because if you're happy for a reason, that reason can go away.

I sing a lot around the house. When my friend is here and he hears me singing, he'll say, "Why so happy, señorita?" I always respond, "Just 'cause!"

There are many things we can do to contribute to our happiness: sleep more, help others, do something because it feels right, eat better (that may mean eat less, it may mean eat more, it may mean choose more nourishing options), wear a bright color, dance, laugh unabashedly, be content with what is, say no, say yes, be bold, be brave, be kind.

"If you choose not to find joy in the snow, you will have less joy in your life but still the same amount of snow."

—Anonymous

Chapter Fourteen

Survivorship

"Important Milestone"
May 11, 2016

T omorrow marks one year since my mastectomy. The passing of time since then is hard to describe. It feels like yesterday and a lifetime ago at once.

When I think about having had a mastectomy, it seems like it was recent. But when I put it into context as having had the surgery right after chemo ended, it seems very long ago.

I suppose that's what happens when so many changes happen in a short period.

Today, I saw my surgeon. She said that things are coming along nicely but that my caregivers can do better when it comes to getting my full range of motion and posture back.

Right now, my left scapula is poking out more than the right, and the muscles along my left side, armpit, and shoulder are still restricted. She was happy to hear that I'm still seeing my physical therapist. She wants me to continue that until I'm fully rehabilitated. She thinks that weak rhomboids are causing the discrepancy from left to right side.

I'm not at all surprised.

All of my muscles are weak. That tends to happen when arm use is restricted for so long. But my therapist and I are becoming more aggressive with my treatment now. I'm able to raise my arm more fully and I have improved rotation of my shoulder. At this stage of treatment, she is doing more orthopedic type of manual therapy on me rather than typical lymphedema treatment. I have had no symptoms of lymphedema.

My PT said that I didn't lose as much range of motion as she thought I might, but still, I want to move freely. So that's what we're working on.

Yesterday, she dry needled at least six different areas on my upper left quadrant. Dry needling is such a strange feeling. There's a sharp burst at first but once the needle is in and the twitches begin, a warming sensation follows and then it relaxes. Today, I'm pretty sore from the manipulation, deep-muscle massage, and needling. It's good for me to continue stretching and drink lots of water to work that out. Pretty much any time I'm sitting idle, I stretch my arms, upper back, and chest.

My surgeon said that she wants to see me again in six months. She said that if I come back to Denver to see my reconstructive surgeon for my next surgery, to schedule an appointment with her because she wants to see me improve.

Do the Right Thing

This Saturday, I'm going to a new hairstylist. It's the same salon where I got my wig last year. It's a wig-design shop as well as a plant-based and cruelty-free salon. The owner had breast cancer once upon a time. And so she understands how to grow hair out and style it through the stages.

Today, the nurse at my surgeon's office said, "I wish I could pull off short hair." I quipped, "I wish I didn't have to." Think, people! This hairstyle was not a choice for me (or other people going through cancer treatment or other diseases). I'm not trying something "new." My hair fell out, handfuls at a time, until I was bald, because the medication that I needed to save my life made it.

Don't get me wrong. I can take a compliment. When my surgeon came in, she said, "Your hair looks great." I said the proper thank-you. And I meant it. I wish people understood. The two options are pretty much: give a short compliment or say nothing.

"The Hardest Part"
June 27, 2016

I am at a point in my recovery where I look largely, well, recovered. But I am told that it will take up to two years for my systems to rebound and my full abilities to return. I believe that, but what's hard for me is that my team hasn't agreed on how exactly to go about that. Butch believes in slow, careful, somewhat passive recovery. My oncologist believes that being physically active every day is important. My PT believes that continual movement of affected muscles will help restore their mobility sooner and more completely.

I have considered all of their points and I have decided this: I will do what I *feel* like my body wants to do.

In the end, isn't that the key?

It's an important lesson I learned in this whole process, to listen to what my body needs. Lately, I've felt like running. So, I do. I don't run far or fast, but that's irrelevant. I run as far as I feel like, as fast as I feel like. Sometimes, I even feel like sprinting short distances. And so, I do.

I run about every other day. I do passive yoga poses every day. I do a more active yoga sequence after running. I haven't been riding my bike consistently yet, but I am ready to. I joined the gym so I can do group exercise classes when I want to or swim. I have some time to take walks after dinner and do some evening bike rides. I'm not overdoing or underdoing it. I am rested and pain free.

I am reminded often when I look at my legs, my arms, my abs that I lost a lot of muscle tone. That is a result of the chemo medications, the fatigue, exhaustion, and bone pain I felt during chemo, the surgeries, the anesthesia, and the radiation. But one major muscle that was dramatically affected that I can't see is my heart muscle. It went through all the things I just mentioned, but additionally, I was on a cardio-toxic chemo drug for a full twelve months. It underwent something that none of my other muscles did, quite to the same degree. So, although I can't see it, my heart muscle is also "flabby."

I am told that exercising the heart muscle to get the medication pumped out helps, so I do lots of activity regularly.

Most of my medical team just met me when I was diagnosed. So, they talk about being active, not sitting around, getting up, and doing something every day. The thing is, they don't really know me. Butch does. He knows that I'm an industrious worker bee. I rarely sit. I clean, cook, do laundry, shop, unpack, rearrange, garden, sweep, water, prune, refill—the list goes on. If there's a verb out there, I do it. So, I think that Butch knows that my tendency would be to overdo it, not underdo it.

Therefore, I do not put pressure on myself to "perform." I'm allowed a pass here and there—in the way that works for me.

"Survivorship"
September 20, 2016

When I see my new medical oncologist (I have moved states), I have a question that I need cleared up. I often hear people talking about how many years they have survived cancer. I love hearing this kind of positive news. But I am a little perplexed. When does one start counting?

I'm not concerned about what number I get to tell people because it's not like I want to give cancer that kind of power over my life. To count years, months, and days from a cancer diagnosis is a little morbid to me. The past is the past.

However, my medical care changes over time. My oncologist in Denver told me that he'd follow up with me every three months for a while, then every six months, then once a year. But what are we counting from? Until recently, it hadn't occurred to me that I didn't know this rather important detail.

Plus, once I was diagnosed, I was given all sorts of stats about three-year survivorship, five-year survivorship, and "extended" survivorship, a.k.a. "life." So, I'd like to know, basically, when I can begin to feel "out of the woods."

I searched for an answer online and quickly regretted it. Not only were the answers unclear, but they were also a little too saccharine for my taste. I just want facts, not a pep talk.

Throughout the treatment process, there were many milestones.

There's the day I was diagnosed: December 3, 2014.

There's the day I began chemo/immunotherapy: December 26, 2014.

There's the day I ended chemo: April 9, 2015.

There's the day of my mastectomy: May 12, 2015.

There's the day that I was told that I had a complete pathologic response to chemotherapy: May 15, 2015.

There's the day that I finished radiation: August 4, 2015.

There's the day I ended immunotherapy: December 17, 2015.

I guess to me, I consider my survivorship to have begun on the day of my diagnosis. Seems logical—I have lived this long since I was first told that I had cancer. I'll be asking this question at my first opportunity.

Until then, business as usual. I'm doing yoga daily to improve the strength, flexibility, and range of motion of my arms, back, and chest.

I will have a positive attitude and remember the best, most-positive, and briefest affirmation I know: I am well.

"Now I Know"
October 31, 2016

When I met with my new oncologist, I asked her about the date that we start counting survivorship from. Well, she counts from the last day of all treatments. She said that for her, she likes to do it that way for two reasons.

1. After all treatment that was prescribed is done it allows us to say, "Okay, we've done what we think is necessary, and now we closely monitor how the body responds." For me, I had a complete pathological response to treatment. Not everyone does. Therefore,

I don't need scans; I don't need MRIs. I do need the close eye of a competent oncologist for several more years. I also need prayers, well wishes, supportive thoughts, positive energy, and good vibes. So, feel free to send some my way whenever I cross your mind. Thanks, and I'll do the same for you.

2. It gives her more time to follow me more closely. Once treatment is complete (for me, it was December 17, 2015), I need to see an oncologist every four months for three years. Then every six months for two years. Then once a year for an indeterminate amount of time. If they were to start counting on my diagnosis day, that would mean that I'm already through two years of seeing someone every four months. But that's not accurate. In that first year, I was seeing all kinds of doctors very frequently and treatment was underway. It wasn't until my pathology came back after surgery that we knew for sure that I had a complete pathological response. And after that, I still underwent six weeks of radiation therapy that ended in August. From there, I received an infusion of immunotherapy every three weeks until December 17, 2015. That is the day from which we begin to think of "survivorship."

"Shout It from the Mountaintops"
November 4, 2016

Whenever a reader of this blog reads past posts, I get a summary of which ones. Then I go back and read them because I have forgotten so many details.

I really love doing that.

I love seeing where I was, how far I've come, how much I've grown, and how content I am in my life now. I can do all the things I missed—*everything*! I feel like shouting from the mountaintops! I am not only living my life again but I'm also living my life better. And it all happened because I just kept taking steps. I had *no* idea what this path looked like. But no knowledge of the path can make up for just putting one foot in front of the other.

"*Danke Schön*, Baby"
November 22, 2016

Here we are in Thanksgiving week. I am taking a few minutes to enumerate, iterate, and codify all the things I'm grateful for (à la Sheldon Cooper). Forgive my sloppy outlining, I never liked it.

I remember hearing once that being thankful without expressing it is like having a gift that is never opened. I'm going to unwrap my gifts, one at a time.

I. My Health

A. I'm thankful for a normal alkaline phosphatase (ALP) level. Yes, you probably won't hear that one around your dinner table on Thursday. But it's true.

- When I started seeing my new primary care doctor in September, she did the usual exam along with blood work and a urinalysis. I've been having no symptoms of anything, but my lab work turned up an abnormality in my blood. My ALP level was outside the normal parameters—which is a common occurrence in people but if it happens between annual appointments, we often never know. I followed my doctor's recommendation to have it tested and then retested for a third time. Upon the final testing, it was back to normal.

- ALP is produced by bones, liver, and colon. Extremely high levels (which I did not have) can be indicative of cancer. Coupled with the following issue, it was best not to chance it. Hence, the importance of retesting and my gratitude for a normal level.

B. I'm thankful for a clear CT scan of my abdomen. At that same doctor's appointment previously mentioned, I had an abnormal urinalysis. There was more than a trace amount of blood found upon three different tests.

- I was referred to a urologist (along with every man over sixty in this city). He said my level was just outside the normal range and didn't think there was a concern but did recommend a CT scan of my abdomen to rule out kidney stones and cancer.

- Bladder cancer is an issue for people who have had strong chemotherapy because the bladder is the last bastion in ridding the body of toxins. The bladder is a holding tank of these toxins. That's why it's important to drink a lot of water and pee often, particularly during chemo.
- Last week, I had the test and got my results about two days later. It is clear. And I am thankful.

C. I am thankful for my physical fitness and ability to return to previously loved activities.

- I do yoga daily, whether at home or at my new, wonderful, amazing, awesome, perfect, fun, exciting yoga studio. Yoga provides me with body movement and so much more. I've met great people, joined a book club, and have tapped into a network of impressively accomplished teachers and stunningly supportive fellow students.
- I walk, jog, cycle, kickbox, do strength training, and just about anything else that interests me because I can. And for that, I am thankful.

II. My Family

All my family, back in one spot. For that, I am thankful.

III. Bettering Myself

I work every day at being a better version of myself. I sometimes backslide, but that's how life works. I know for sure that I'm a better mom and wife than I used to be. I'm learning what it means to be me and not just what I mean to other people. For all the ways that I'm discovering myself, I am thankful.

IV. North Carolina

Moving here has been a challenge. I miss Colorado, but I believe that I was brought here for a reason. For a while, I was trying to figure out what that reason was. But I realized that that is a fool's errand. The reason will unfold for me. I don't have to excavate. It will become clear over time.

I am enjoying new restaurants, new breweries, new people, new adventures, new dinner guests, our new home, and even a new car.

V. Daily Gifts

I read once about the idea of imagining waking up tomorrow and having everything that you didn't give thanks for today be gone. Holy shit. I'm thankful for *everything*!

- I'm thankful for contact lenses, medicine, hair products, food, farmers, garbage collectors, the sun, vacuum cleaners, electricity, fire, wheels, books, shoes, coats, blankets, pillows, beds, showers, chocolate, wine, games . . . you get the point. I try to be thankful for things as I use them. It's easier than trying to list them.

- Often, we let a five-minute hassle with our cars ruin our day. And we forget the million things leading up to that that went *right*. I'm getting better at focusing on things that go right.

"Yesterday Was December 3"
December 4, 2016

That's the date in 2014 when I was given the news that I had breast cancer.

But it wasn't really all that "new"—I had known for about six weeks that something was very wrong. I was the one who found the lump in my breast and under my armpit. I am the one who went to the doctor to say that something was wrong. I was the one who told them. But they confirmed it on December 3, 2014.

So, how did I commemorate the day yesterday? With celebrations, of course!

I celebrate because, first, I can. I'm here, and I can look back at those two years and be grateful for so stinking much.

Second, I celebrate because, to me, hearing that I had cancer was a green light. It was "go time." It was permission to move forward to finding an oncologist and a surgeon. It was time to begin treating the illness. It was time to begin healing. And so, I did.

What did I do to celebrate? Lots.

First, I got up early before the rest of my family, and I had quiet space to ease into my day. I readied myself for a slow flow class at my yoga studio. It was a great class. I often feel that the intention set by the instructor hits the nail on the head in a way so perfect that it feels personal. Personal enough that I wonder for a minute, "Maybe she *can* hear my thoughts?"

I accept serendipity, and I devote myself to gratitude in my practice.

Yoga was followed by a yummy breakfast and a long and meaningful conversation with a good friend.

I came home to Michael and Zach neck-deep in leaves. The leaves—my god, the leaves. What else could I do but leave? So, I got ready and headed back out to the Wellness Open House at my yoga studio.

It was a nice event with local artists and vendors, but the pièce de résistance? An opportunity to have one-on-one sessions with yoga therapists and Reiki practitioners. Maybe needless to say, but I took the opportunity to have a session.

I talked with the yoga therapist about my arm, chest, and shoulder issues in the wake of my treatment. She immediately knew what to do. And she got to work. I immediately felt relief. Simply by having someone who knows what to do and how to help me continue to heal was enough.

She gave me a list of exercises and a mantra to repeat while I do them. I scheduled another appointment with her for tomorrow after my morning yoga. I went to the open house to find Christmas gifts for some ladies in my life and I ended up finding this gift for myself.

Finally, last night, Michael and Zach and I went to the local German beer garden for dinner and the Weihnachtsmarkt (German Christmas market). We had a blast. We shopped, met up with friends, and drank beer until last call with our friends and another couple. We enjoy the German lifestyle—community tables, food we love, plenty of beer, and even more conversation and laughter.

We crawled into bed around midnight, exhausted from the day but so very thankful for every last minute of it and for the last two years of my life.

Life is good.

"I Am Pissed"
December 6, 2016

And I am sad. I need to get this off my chest.

When I went through cancer treatment, the cancer medical community was on top of it, with cutting-edge chemotherapy drugs, state-of-the-art surgical techniques, and the latest findings in dosimetry. But sadly, that's where it stops in Western medicine.

Before I get into this, let me say that I am so freaking happy to be here that I find words inadequate. However, I can't ignore this.

What has me in such a lather today is my yoga therapy work that I just started. I love it. I found a real gem in my therapist, and I'm happy beyond measure to have stumbled upon this yoga studio. This kind of therapy is far beyond the reaches of the physical therapy I received in Colorado. While my PT there was masterful at completely eliminating any effects of my lymph node removal and kept my upper left quadrant movable and flexible throughout radiation, the insurance company severely limited her scope of treatment.

Why is yoga therapy different? Because she can work with my entire body. She can look at the way I walk and stand, how I move not only my shoulders and chest but also my pelvis and hips. She has given me exercises that have had a greater impact on my mobility in three short days than anything I was doing in the past eighteen months combined.

So, why doesn't every woman who's gone through breast cancer know about this?

And that's why I'm mad and sad.

Why doesn't the cancer medical community treat the whole patient?

I remember at the very beginning of treatment getting a call from the American Cancer Society. The woman asked me if I had any concerns, needed resources, financial help, etc. This conversation happened in December of 2014—before I'd had even one dose of chemotherapy. At the time, I felt fine. Like *perfectly* fine. So, questions like this were not only fruitless but they also didn't make sense to me.

I had no idea what I was in for. No one does. How can you possibly know? Everyone is different. Everyone has their own experience. And you can't possibly guess what you need before you know. I needed this call months later from someone equipped to provide holistic care.

Even beyond that, why doesn't the cancer medical community treat the whole family? I'm not the only one who suffered during that process. My kids were scared, my husband was run ragged by all my needs, and Kerrianne took more vacation time than she probably had to be able to come to Denver and help.

The thing is their scars are acknowledged by the cancer medical community. I heard it all the time; "Cancer is hard on everyone in the family," they'd say. But that was it. End of discussion. No offer of help or ideas of where to find it.

It's truly mind-boggling that I sought all my complementary treatment on my own and paid for it on my own. While I was going through it, I was happy to have allies on my side. My whole team was amazing. But the piece that's missing in the cancer medical community is that once treatment ceases, care of the patient ceases—and that is wrong.

Our medical system is deficient in so many ways it's maddening. And it's now that I'm past the treatment that I have the luxury of fuming. No one should have to suffer during cancer treatment and recovery. Options are available, but the patient has to be aware and able to afford them out of pocket.

In 2015, I spent $17,000 on out-of-pocket expenses. And that is a lot of money. But if you take, for example, the cost of one chemo treatment it's a drop in the bucket. One of my treatments cost $60,000. I had six of those. And then twelve more of a single medication. Chemo lasted for a year for me. I had three surgeries. I had a hospital room that cost my insurance company $137,000 for one night. (Not shitting you, I have the bill.) I had biopsies, PET scans, MRIs, and mammograms. I had blood work and echocardiograms. I had six weeks of daily radiation. I had weekly physical therapy. And this was all covered by my insurance. My insurance company spent well over a million dollars on my treatment in 2015. So, my question is this: what's another $17,000 that would *dramatically* improve a patient's quality of life?

Don't fool yourself, it all comes down to dollars and cents.

They can't charge $60,000 for yoga therapy. It's not a profitable business model.

I don't mean to be cynical but it feels true. In the cancer medical community, the focus is on treating the disease. Once that is done, further recovery is out of their hands. They may support it, but they don't provide it or even information on how to get it—or what *it* even is.

My oncologist used to ask me what I'm doing to stay well and recover. I'd tell him, and he'd say things like, "Well, that certainly can't hurt." And he was on to the next question.

I don't know the answers here, but it seems like more patients need to take the initiative and demand better care. And more doctors need to treat the patients like an ally and not just their job.

If I can offer some pieces of advice to anyone who is going through treatment, they are these:

- **Take probiotics.** Do it now. Twice daily. And do it at least until you finish chemo. You can find it almost everywhere.
- **Move while you're recuperating in bed.** Leg lifts, bicycles, whatever feels good.
- **Get a wig.** It feels better to look like yourself.
- **Stop eating sugar in all forms,** except fresh fruit, if you can tolerate fresh fruit.
- **Walk when you feel good.**
- **Eat when you feel good.**
- **Sit outside in the sun when you feel good.**
- **Get over being disappointed.** People in your life might disappear upon hearing the word "cancer." Focus on the unexpected blessings you get from everyone else.

- **Get acupuncture and try other traditional Chinese medicine.**
- **Do yoga.**
- **Breathe.**
- **Lastly, find the joy.** Some days it may be hard. But it's there. You'll see it, even if you have to squint.

"December—A Big Month"
December 14, 2016

This is a big month for me.

As I mentioned in a previous post, the third marked the date of my cancer diagnosis. And this week holds two important dates.

Monday, the twelfth, was the six-month anniversary of our move to North Carolina. So much has happened in that time.

I feel like it's been a roller coaster. At first, I was excited and ready. And then once reality set in, I felt lonely. My daughter, Aspen, is in Colorado. My son, Zach, is at school every day. And for the first time in about fifteen years, Michael is working in an office again. I got really used to having him home all the time, if he wasn't traveling. It was awesome. So, there's been a lot of adjustment.

Luckily, the loneliness phase has been short-lived!

I have quit my job (with a heavy heart) so that I can pursue my German language degree. I have a weekly class right now (that I love) where I'm one of only two students! We are taught by a great teacher who was born in the Netherlands and speaks Dutch, German, and English. I have a new yoga studio, with lots of great teachers and students. I have a book club that I enjoy. I found some of my favorite places. I know where I'm going without the GPS.

It's not really the places; it's the people. I'm feeling connected again. I've met some amazing people who have popped up out of nowhere and changed my life. I've always felt that there are no coincidences, and that belief has been reaffirmed for me recently.

I believe it's better to go forward than back. I had to relearn that in these past six months.

For a while, I was busy trying to create a new life in all the ways I could think of. Some of those things worked out well, some did not. And once I realized that I was doing a whole lot of trying, I decided to stop trying so hard. It's been since then that tremendous things have happened for me.

I had to let go in order to receive. You see, if you keep holding on to the old stuff, there's no room for the new. And that new stuff is the good stuff, the surprising stuff, the stuff you didn't even know to ask for.

The second important date this week is Saturday, the seventeenth. It's the first anniversary of the end of my cancer treatment. In all, the medical treatments lasted a year—from diagnosis to chemotherapy to surgery to radiation. This is a big milestone to call to mind as I continue to regain strength and cardiovascular fitness and balance.

Balance is key. It's been missing in my body and in my life. So that's what I practice both on the mat and off. Yoga practice is nothing more (and nothing less) than a big ol' metaphor for life.

Now that my pendulum has swung far in one direction and swung back the other way, it's finally beginning to rest in the center, with mild rocking, and always coming back to center.

What am I going to do to celebrate? I'm going to be mindfully joyful. I'm not going to plan anything. Just take life as it comes. And enjoy every second with gratitude in my heart.

That's hard to do as "The Mom," particularly in December. I've been shopping and driving and planning and booking and cooking and decorating and ordering and calling and wrapping and all the "ings" you can imagine.

This morning, I set the intention to stop.

I'm done with errands. I'm done with plans. I'm just going to have fun. I'm going to have a *merry* Christmas! I'm going to have a *joyful* holiday! I'm going to have a *happy* new year!

I'm going to accept invitations. I'm going to attend dinner parties. I'm going to watch my favorite Christmas movies (*Love Actually*, *Elf*, and *The Grinch*). I'm going to color. I'm going to ring in the new year. There is a lot to *do* this time of year, but while I am involved in those things, I will be mindful to *be* . . . happy, joyful, merry, and grateful. Many of us get stressed out over time, money, commitments, and we forget the important stuff—our families, our friends, our abundance. That's where the true joy is.

"Untethering"
January 17, 2017

I'm out of energy for being angry at/saddened by/disappointed by/frustrated with/confused about/overwhelmed by the medical community. It's become clear to me that each person has to be their own advocate and seek information for themselves, like I have. With the internet being what it is, it's so much easier to find information.

Remember to ask questions. Inform yourself. Seek options. Be open. Know that thoughts are more powerful than anything. Find the joy. Believe that love conquers all.

The Untethered Soul

I've been reading this book with my book group, and it has taught me to let it go. All of it. I'm done trying to figure out if I'm "safe." Who is? Right now, I'm healthy and happy. And that's all any of us have—the present moment. I'm moving forward. It's possible to move on without being completely done with something. I still have to have checkups. And I am still helping my body do its magical, wonderful thing. And I'm done feeling like this time is a continuation of my treatment.

So, I just decided—I'm done. I've come up with a new wording to explain to my new medical professionals that I went through treatment and what my current status is, and that wording does not involve the word "cancer."

"Cancer free." Ugh. It's an awful thing to drag around. So, I'm not. I'm setting it down. And moving on. Free of worry. Free of the burden.

As a friend recently reminded me, it's time to drive fast and take chances while I can.

Free Your Mind, and the Rest Will Follow

I'd like to talk for a minute about my recent craniosacral therapy treatment. I've had only one treatment, but it was life-changing. Definitely worth checking out.

During my first treatment, she drained my liver and kidneys. She helped rid my body of the remaining anesthesia. She released the heat of radiation. She cleaned out the brain fog.

Since that treatment, I've slept. I no longer get headaches after long sessions of studying German. It wasn't because German is hard (it is); it was because my brain was still repairing from the cognitive impairment caused by chemo and anesthesia. Gone. Shoulder pain? Gone. Muscle weakness? Gone. Restriction? Gone.

Know what else is gone? Feeling like it's my job to convince people around me that it's not voodoo, hogwash, or witchcraft. It's all there. You just have to open your mind.

I may be a late adopter of technology, social media, television shows, and more. But I'm the first to adopt ideas, possibilities, opportunities—the things that matter.

"Dear Erika on May 30, 2015"
May 30, 2017

I come to you from the future to say, the answer to all of your questions is yes. Yes! Yes. Yep.

I know that you just finished six rounds of chemotherapy and are only a couple of weeks past a bilateral mastectomy. I know that you still have to face six weeks of radiation after starting the process of reconstruction. I know that you have to get immuno-therapy infusions every three weeks fourteen more times. And I know that more surgery will follow next year. Still, I am here to tell you—the answer is YES!

Yes, you will run comfortably again. Your knees will benefit from the exercise and your hips will appreciate the movement. Your bones will reap the effects of the impact and continue to strengthen and build. Your heart will beat like your own again and your breathing will be slow and strong. When, you ask? Tuesday, May 30, 2017. Not someday. Today.

Yes, your body will look like yours again. And feel like yours again. Your hair will fall in soft curls to your shoulders. And you will have ordered a two-piece bathing suit for your upcoming European vacation. When, you ask? Today.

Yes, you will move like *you* again. Your arms are free. Your chest is open. Your back is strong. Your lats are toned. Your legs are sturdy. Your triceps are independent. Yoga, cycling, hiking, running—whatever you choose will be available to you. Today and every other day.

Your heart will recover from the powerful, risky, necessary medication that is infused into your body every twenty-one days. It is resilient. Those echocardiograms? Keep getting them as often as you're told to. Everything turns out fine. Your heart, while its condition is reset to zero, recovers. It no longer pounds like a kick drum when you rise from bed. Your pulse no longer throbs in your throat from walking up a flight of stairs. You'll hike and run and do challenging yoga poses.

You will be satisfied because you realize that giving a shit isn't your style. You will run down a long and open lane and feel good. And you'll thank yourself for heading out on this run. And suddenly, you'll realize that everything feels good—your knees, your femurs, your hips, your heart, your lungs, with sweat pouring off your forehead onto your eyelashes (yes, eyelashes!). And you'll find yourself grinning. And when you do, you'll chuckle out loud because you're just so damn glad that you can do this. And you don't care who sees you.

You are in this place, living your dharma, because you're grateful, and therefore you're happy. You're happy for all that has happened. And—wait for it—for all that *hasn't* happened. (Mind = blown!)

You're grateful that you now realize that "this, too, shall pass" is not just a saying. It's the truest thing you know for sure. And because of the impermanence of all things, you appreciate life that much more.

You're content because you know that only after the lowest of lows can you experience the highest of highs. And guess what? You get to decide what makes you feel high! It's fantastic. Learn

German? Sure. Take a five-week trip to Germany? Don't mind if I do. Get a degree in German? Okay, I'll start in August. Continue a path of spiritual evolution that awakens your soul and invigorates your being? I thought you'd never ask.

You're confident in your own skin. You will be running twelve-minute miles. And those feel sweet. You won't feel like you must make excuses for why you're not "performing" better. Pfft! Screw performance. Running gives you what you need.

You will forgive the people who have disappointed you in this process. You'll realize that they're only human, and they weren't meant to accompany you on this path. They have their own path, which isn't meant for you either. You'll be glad about that and, in some cases, downright tickled.

This is all true because you endured. The task of recovery is daunting but, you stuck with it. You are patient, you are kind, you are supportive, you are tenacious, you are optimistic, you are unrelenting. You have resolve. Your heart is open, and your soul is pure. And so, you are free.

You will wake up on Tuesday, May 30, 2017, and you will go for a run like it's no big whoop. Just lace up your shoes and head out for a few miles, because you've been getting ready for this day, and it's finally here!

"Today, I'm Going to Talk about My Boobs"
October 24, 2017

After all, that's how this all got started, right? But I haven't really addressed my boobs much after the reconstruction. Today, I shall.

In writing this blog, I have come to know some wonderful women who have also been affected by breast cancer. Some have had it themselves; some are concerned that it could happen to them. We have talked about all sorts of things: the meaning of life, the importance of healthy eating, and the job of raising a family. But most never ask me about my boobs, nor I about theirs.

A few have asked, and I'm very willing to discuss the reconstruction process with them. But I wonder if the rest think that it's too private. For me, it isn't. I feel that it's my privilege to share what I've experienced.

I wish I'd known someone—*anyone*—who could have told me how the reconstruction process goes. My surgeon did, of course, but he's a dude and never experienced it himself. So, I take his medical advice for all it's worth. But as for the psychological and emotional side, I had to figure that out step by step.

I'll start by saying this: I love my new boobs. I love them as much today as I did the first time I looked down and saw them. They are a great size. They look real. I didn't imagine that they'd be so natural looking.

But for some strange reason, I've been concealing them. I don't dress like a nun, but I've been hesitant to wear more revealing clothes—except for when I really psych myself up and convince myself that I can "get away with it." I feel that way even about clothes that I owned *before* my surgery.

I've had this gnawing reminder in the back of my head: they're not real and when people see me, they'll know they're not real. And while it may be true that people know they're not real, no one seems to care—especially my husband. I guess if they look like boobs and feel like boobs, they must be boobs!

Well, I've come to a conclusion: I'm going to stop concealing them, for a number of reasons. First, I am already aware that they're not my own breasts. Exceptionally aware. Second, many women out there experience less-than-satisfactory reconstruction. I've seen pictures that my surgeon has "fixed." It's sad how bad some results really are. My results are top-notch, so I have no reason to worry that people will notice them. Third, I underwent a year-long reconstruction process so that I would look like myself again. Why do all that work and go through all that pain just to hide and worry? Lastly, they're a reminder to me—the proof, if you will.

Now, while I don't need to prove to anyone that I had breast cancer, I do go for long periods without thinking about it. And that's fine—even good. I have a life and my health, and I'm grateful for it all. But sometimes when I see myself in a mirror, I'm reminded. I don't get sad or mad. Instead, I'm reminded that I'm capable of difficult things. I'm worthy of beautiful things. And I'm resourceful enough to handle all of life's challenges.

One of the physical side effects of a mastectomy is slouched posture. Women tend to round their shoulders and hunch forward when their torso undergoes trauma. It takes work to reclaim the posture of a straight spine with a forward heart and shoulder blades placed on the back. It's a posture I practice daily on and off the mat. I practice it when I run even.

I've noticed that when I run, I tend to look at my shoes. That body positioning causes a domino effect of poor function. I breathe less fully, I am not mindful of my surroundings, and I round my shoulders forward. I've begun to make a deal with myself that I won't look at my shoes for a whole run. I look forward, with my chin on a shelf, ears over shoulders, shoulder blades on my back behind my heart, and the heads of my arm bones relaxed. It felt strange at first, like I was running with my chest sticking out. But that's not how it looks at all. I'm just used to shielding.

I like thinking of it as running wholeheartedly. We say things like this all the time: her heart wasn't in it, or she believed it wholeheartedly. So that's what I'm doing now, living life wholeheartedly and not hiding behind anything.

Toe the Line

I decided a few months ago that I wanted to train for a half marathon again. Now, I'm up to an hour of running, and I feel confident that by the time the race I'm targeting in March arrives, I will be ready. It's been ten years since I did this distance. And it was before I underwent all the cancer treatment, so I'm cutting myself some slack. I'm slower than I used to be. So right now, my goal is to finish. As I continue in the training process, I'll figure out what a realistic time goal will be.

"Chemotherapy"
November 16, 2017

This past weekend, I met a very nice guy whose wife just finished a four-week course of radiation and a lumpectomy for breast cancer. I said how sorry I was to hear that she was going through it. He thanked me and talked about how hard it had been to face his wife's diagnosis. He continued to say how thankful they were that she didn't have to go through chemo. He talked about the fact that it's *so* bad for you that the doctors weigh the risks of it against the risks of the cancer. So, it must be bad. Just awful. Right? That's what we hear, see, and pass on at least.

I've talked about my truth regarding chemo before, and I'm about to do it again because it bears repeating:

The truth is, I'm grateful for it. Every last drop of it.

It's powerful. It's serious. But you know what else it is? It's necessary and . . . it's *possible*! Before having had chemo, I used to think that it was barely doable. I had even heard, "Let's hope it kills the cancer before it kills you!"

Wow.

In fairness, chemo was not easy. No walk in the park. But can we please stop all the fear around it? Particularly those among us who have no actual idea. Please.

When you think about chemo, what are your immediate images? Let me guess—baldness and vomiting? Chances are, I'm right for most of you. Did you ever think about why we think these things? It's because when the media, movie directors, or even hospitals want to show the face of cancer, they show a bald one. It's a striking image—nearly unmistakable. And vomiting? How dramatic! That makes a great scene. We've all been there, on our knees in front of the toilet, feeling like every last ounce of whatever awfulness entered us is emerging with a force that you couldn't stop if you tried. Maybe your experience wasn't due to chemo, maybe it was a bad flu or too many tequila shots, but we know what it feels like, and so we think we can relate.

But guess what?

Not everyone loses their hair. (I did.) And not everyone pukes. (I did not.) For me, most of those months I spent with grinding, unrelenting nausea, stomach pain, and diarrhea that left me with a permanent feeling of disgust.

The fact is that chemo has just as many invisible symptoms as it does obvious ones. And for all the side effects it causes, it has one undeniable main effect—it kills cancer cells.

I understand that it's not effective for everyone. Sometimes, the cancer is too advanced, or too aggressive, or existing chemotherapy medications don't work on a particular type of cancer. And for those reasons, I am hopeful for better treatments to be found.

I remember hearing for the first time that I had to undergo chemo. I was dumbstruck, feeling so much more scared of chemo than any other part of the process. More than bilateral mastectomy, more than radiation—more than the cancer itself! I had images of dizzying episodes of vomiting and extreme weight loss and other unknown uncontrolled symptoms that would leave me with IVs and hospital beds. Until that point, I had no personal experience with chemo. My mom had had it years ago, but I did not see her daily while she was undergoing it. I knew that it made her dreadfully tired. And I knew that she threw up once and lost her hair. But it was not her experience that instilled this fear in me. It was all the "other" stuff I'd heard.

Please don't misunderstand me. I know that no one *wants* chemotherapy. But for some of us, we have little other choice. We must undergo the process if we wish to be healthy enough to live a full life. Please don't make it worse for us. Have sympathy. Try to empathize, even. If you can't, at the very least shut up. Please.

For those who are facing the possibility, know this: chemo is to be taken just like everything else in the world—one day at a time. The symptoms don't happen all at once. And they don't last forever. They can be strong. But so are you.

For those of us who have had successful chemotherapy treatment, holy cow, I'm thankful. Gratitude—nothing but complete and utter gratitude. It was all worth it. Every last drop.

"Don't Suffer Needlessly"
November 19, 2017

A couple of weeks ago, I decided to join four or five social media groups for women dealing with a current or past breast cancer diagnosis. I thought it would be a good opportunity to hear from women who are in my position as well as a chance to give back any advice or perspective I've gained in my nearly three-year experience.

Almost as quickly as I joined, I hid the groups. There were a lot of eye-opening posts to say the least. There are two topics I've seen a lot about: post-mastectomy soreness and skin care during radiation. I hope that I can shed a little light and possibly eliminate some suffering. Please share this information if you find it useful.

Soreness after Mastectomy

After a mastectomy (particularly a bilateral mastectomy), the entire torso may be sore to some degree, depending on your pain tolerance. Why? Because breasts are not external objects that are simply removed. Incisions are made and the surgeon's hands and instruments are placed under the skin all the way up to the collar bones just below the chin because breast tissue is not contained solely in the "cup" of the breast. It's all along the entire chest wall from clavicle to bottom of the ribs and side to side. They do a very involved procedure they call "scraping." It can leave the body feeling sore. I hope that doctors are fully explaining this to patients, but that's not what I read in these groups.

Skin Care during Radiation

There are radiation oncologists who "allow" patients to use skin care products during treatment. I urge women who find themselves in need of radiation to find one of these doctors. I saw some pictures this week of a woman who was severely burned. Others were commenting that they were "allowed" to use cornstarch only. I almost cried.

When I was about to undergo treatment, I met with three radiation oncologists. The first was just a scary person in general. I wouldn't have gone to her for a manicure let alone lifesaving treatment. So, I honestly can't remember what she said. Bad vibes.

The second was the radiation oncologist I ultimately chose. His nurse talked with me extensively about treatment and all the products that they approve for my use during the weeks of treatment if my skin was left clean and clear during the actual treatment.

I really liked this doctor and his staff, but I got a third opinion because the first was so bad I almost couldn't count her.

The third was equally a nightmare. She insisted that I use nothing on my skin for the entire six weeks. I would be permitted to wash with a run-of-the-mill soap and use cornstarch. I'll tell you what I think of this soap and cornstarch.

This soap is actually marketed as a "beauty bar." It's meant to moisturize more than clean. And the quality of its moisturizers is very low grade. It has a list of more than a dozen ingredients, most of which are preservatives and synthetic detergents. It's a bunch of crap. It's not the kind of stuff I'd put on my skin even if I weren't going through radiation, so why start now? Second, cornstarch is used to keep the skin dry. Dry? Really? That is not at all what is needed. Chemicals and dryness. No thanks.

In the end, I went with the radiation oncologist who understood skin care. One of the best decisions I've ever made.

During radiation, I was under the beam for about fifty-five seconds, which is typical. It doesn't have to be long to be effective. The skin on my upper left quadrant was to be completely clean and clear. My radiation time was 10:45 a.m. so I'd shower and go to my appointment without using any products on that area. But, in my purse, I had a naturopathic apothecary.

In the changing room after treatment, I applied a mixture of calendula cream and emu oil. Calendula cream comes from the calendula flower, a member of the daisy family and often called marigold. It has myriad benefits. Here's what I found from OnOurFarms.com about it: "Calendula creams and washes are used to disinfect minor wounds and to treat infections of the skin. The antibacterial and immunostimulant properties of the plant make it extremely useful in treating slow-healing cuts and cuts in people who have compromised immune systems." Boom. Done. It can be found online, in stores, or maybe your local naturopath has it in stock.

Emu oil is extracted from the adipose (fat) tissue of emus. Studies suggest it can decrease inflammation, improve wounds, and nourish and hydrate skin damaged by radiation treatment. It's not as hard to find as it sounds. I got mine at a nationwide vitamin and supplement chain. It's also online.

As soon as treatment was over, I squeezed a generous amount of calendula cream into my palm and mixed in emu oil. I then applied it to the entire area of my chest (more on coverage area in a minute). I took my time and followed the nurse's advice about being gentle and working in the direction of lymphatic drainage.

Then, I'd reapply later in the day. Around three or four p.m., I repeated the process.

At bedtime, I used a whole different product. It's called tamanu oil. It's smelly, it stains everything a sort of greenish color, and it's sticky. But it's *so* worth it. I simply sacrificed two T-shirts and a pillowcase that I tossed after treatment was over.

Tamanu oil comes from a nut grown in the South Pacific and has been used for centuries to clear up almost any skin condition. This recommendation came to me from my plastic surgeon. I bought mine at my local health food store. It's also online.

Now, here's the important part:

It worked. Like, crazy good. You know how I know? Because I accidentally did a scientific study.

I didn't realize that the beam went as far back to where the back of my armpit meets my shoulder blade. So, I wasn't applying any of the creams back there. Somewhere around the end of treatment, I had a relatively small (a few inches) but painful, deep burn there. It was right where the arm moves and swings against the body, so I felt it far before I saw it. And I was surprised to realize that the beam was being aimed that far back (cancer cells had been in my nodes).

Once I discovered it, I had to use silver sulfadiazine cream to prevent infection. It's an antibiotic that is used to treat second- and third-degree burns. And once the sore closed over, I used my other formulas there. So, I know—for a fact—that had I not used this regimen, I would've suffered needlessly.

The doctors who didn't "allow" skin care during treatment said that the reason is that they didn't want the radiation to be blocked. Hey! There's some news! You can block radiation with calendula cream and raspberries, folks! (Yes, one doctor told me that there are too many good antioxidants in berries to eat them during treatment).

Here's the list in short form: immediately after treatment, I used a blend of calendula cream and emu oil. Six hours later, I reapplied. At bedtime, I used tamanu oil. In the morning, it was all washed off in the shower in time for the next treatment.

My skin looks amazing. Not only did the products work, but the application gave me at least three opportunities a day to massage the tissue and keep it mobile.

"Remember to Celebrate"
May 15, 2018

Today, I am celebrating a fantastic milestone. Three years ago today, I got some of the best news of my life, and it was contained in two words: No cancer.

It was only three days after my bilateral mastectomy, and my surgeon called. She left a message. She cut right to the chase to tell me I'd had a complete pathological response.

I saved that voicemail for a long time. But even now that I don't have it, I can still hear her voice and remember how I felt at that moment.

I still had quite a road ahead of me. I had been through six months of chemotherapy and a bilateral mastectomy. And I still had radiation therapy, six more months of infusions, and reconstruction ahead. But at that point, I knew that the disease was gone and everything from that point on was about prevention and healing.

These three years have been filled with so much: travel, education, opportunities, a move, time spent with my family, and lots of opportunities to be grateful.

Having a complete pathological response to chemotherapy was the best possible outcome, and I'm grateful every day. About 60 percent of patients in my shoes have this result. So, it was by no means a guarantee but somehow, I always felt I would be one of the lucky ones. I could feel it in my bones.

"*A bird sitting on a branch is never afraid of the branch breaking, because its trust is not on the branch but on its own wings.*"

—Charlie Wardle

Chapter Fifteen

Where I Am Now

"At Peace"
September 27, 2022

Yesterday, I met with my new oncologist in Montana (I've moved again). Despite driving three hours for the appointment, it was beyond worth it.

I didn't have to go three hours away to find an oncologist. There are oncologists closer to where I live now, but when I started the process of finding one, I was living in that city and thought I would be for a while. And given that I've needed to see my previous oncologist only once a year, an annual three-hour drive didn't seem unmanageable, so I kept the appointment.

After meeting him, I think I would walk five hundred miles and I would walk five hundred more just to be his patient.

Hyperbole? Only slightly.

He's exactly what I was looking for: caring, personable, invested in integrative medicine (perhaps most importantly), smart, reasonable, concerned about the whole person, and lastly, funny and interesting to talk to.

It's no mistake that I wound up with him. I sought him, as well as one can seek via the internet. His profile discussed understanding that patients are in a "vulnerable situation" and that he treats the whole patient—from physical well-being to mental and spiritual health. I was sold.

Couldn't have scripted it any better (unless it had said "Erika" in place of "patient").

He gushed over my previous "complete response" to my treatments. He said that seven years out without relapse is all but a guarantee of no future relapse. He said that the form of cancer I had was somewhat aggressive and if it were to have returned, it would have within the first (probably) three years.

I will celebrate my seven-year milestone on December 17 with a renewed understanding and increased gratitude (if that's even possible).

We talked about meditation, thankfulness, psychotherapy, massage therapies (craniosacral, lymphatic drainage, myofascial), acupuncture, supplements, quality of life, kids, skate skiing, and sushi. We discussed which of these modalities will continue to serve me and I will reintroduce to my life to help with my current health and comfort (sushi chief among them).

We talked about my plan under the umbrella of oncology care, and it's basically up to me. He believes that clinically there is no reason to continue following me. I don't do scans and blood work and all the stuff you might imagine at these appointments. Rather, they look at my overall health and top it off with a manual breast exam. He said that as long as my PCP does this once a year, then he's more than comfortable with that. He left the door open for me to send questions and schedule as I feel comfortable. For now, I've decided that I'd like to go again next September. I will see my new PCP in October and get all the blood draws, vaccinations, breast exam, and referrals taken care of at that time.

In retrospect, I wish I could've recorded at least parts of my conversation with "Dr. Dreamy" yesterday. I jest, of course, but the thought of having his voice on repeat saying that I'm all but guaranteed no relapse based on my pathology and treatment outcome is deeply, eternally, life-affirmingly reassuring.

Chapter Sixteen

On Menopause

I had wanted to write a blog post on menopause for a long time, but I never did. I put it off for a few reasons. I procrastinated partly because there was no logical place to stop and draw conclusions, find the perfect things to say, and share final thoughts on what worked for me. Menopause is an ongoing, and probably never-ending, fact of my life now. I'm still trying to figure out how to deal with some aspects of it. But I decided I can share what I've tried and what has worked so far.

Additionally, people haven't traditionally been willing to talk about menopause even in what I'll call regular circumstances. I believe there are many cultural, societal, religious, and gender-based reasons for that. It's been called "The Change" and been depicted not so kindly in movies and on TV. I've heard men refer to it as "men-on-pause," which is so cringey because there's no worse time than when a woman is experiencing a major event in her life for uninformed men to make it about them. Fortunately, the tide is starting to turn. I'm now seeing ads on TV about the hypothalamus and vasomotor symptoms of menopause. There are medications to manage them, bioidentical hormones that can be taken, and support groups for women to know they're not alone. I want to be part of this changing dynamic.

Lastly, I didn't necessarily want to publicize certain very private aspects of my life. It's hard to talk about things like your sex life, slowed cognition, and difficulty maintaining weight. It doesn't take any more than that to start feeling like people look at you differently, for employers to consider such a woman too old and unemployable, and to feel like spoiled milk. I went into cancer feeling young, healthy, vibrant, and that a future of many decades of the same was all but guaranteed. Menopause changed that, at least for a while. I want to let other women know it's okay to talk about these natural changes without shame.

The topic of menopause may seem out of place in a book about cancer. Trust me, it's not. I would've thought so before as well, but now I know that menopause was by far the most glossed-over aspect of my cancer care. Chemo medications can, and in my case irreversibly did, induce premature onset of menopause, with all the attendant symptoms and health risks. I was simply blindsided by the full impact of it. I believe it's an equally important factor affecting quality of life and long-term survivorship that should be as thoroughly understood as the cancer treatments themselves.

Unfortunately, I uncovered yet another area where cancer care is too narrowly focused on the disease and the affected organ(s). When people consider breast cancer survivors, it's not just about breasts. In fact, the breasts are only one consideration. Rather, the whole body, along with the mind and spirit, are affected. And menopause is one of the few truly interminable effects that a woman can experience due to surviving breast cancer. I aim to expand the conversation.

How My Menopause Began

When I went to the hospital on December 23, 2014, to have my port implanted in my arm to receive chemotherapy treatments, I was on my period. I hadn't thought too much about that fact. Even during a month when I was stressed and worried, my period came, like it always had: about every twenty-eight days, unceremoniously, for the last thirty years with no signs of it slowing down or stopping anytime soon.

At that point, I was forty-three, had had two kids (both teenagers by then), and had long been done with pregnancy and childbirth. In fact, my husband and I decided that he should have a vasectomy to confirm our decision when our younger child was two years old.

So, when I was told that the medications I'd be given to eradicate the cancer would also affect my reproductive system, all I thought was, *Well, I was done having kids anyway.*

Yes, the end of childbearing is one of the things that menopause causes, but the full extent of menopause and the permanent effects it can have on the body completely escaped me. I hadn't had to consider it yet. It wasn't on my radar.

I proceeded blindly, after next to no discussion with my medical team about menopause. I remember two scenarios with two different caregivers that were nearly identical. They went like this: "We can harvest your eggs if you and your husband are still wanting to expand your family." That appeared to be the most important question regarding menopause and my answer was simple. "No thanks. We're done having kids."

Without egg harvesting to delay treatment, three days after my port implant, I went in for my first chemo treatment, still on my period. It was the last one I'd ever have.

While that might sound like a burden had been lifted, it was anything but. It felt like hitting a brick wall. Everything stopped. My body was extremely, suddenly, and undeniably fully done with that part of life.

No more periods. No more womanly hormones. No more fertility.

Then the menopause symptoms began. Alongside them, the chemo side effects were in full swing: my hair fell out, then my eyebrows and eyelashes thinned; I was tired, weak, and my memory was impaired. I didn't look or feel anything like my old self. And soon, the final blow would be dealt—in a few short months, I'd have no more breasts. I felt stripped of my femininity. I felt defeated and empty. Even if I were to survive this disease, I wondered, *Who am I anymore?*

Most women get years to ease into the idea and symptoms of perimenopause. Hormones start to decline, periods start to space themselves out, a hot flash or two begin to happen. The innate ebb and flow can pace itself out for years or a full decade or more before the process is complete.

Not for me. Everything stopped on a dime. I had no time to adjust or come to terms. The chemo medications I needed made menopause inevitable and, ultimately, irreversible. Following a steady decline in estrogen, I tested post-menopausal within about eighteen months.

Getting Relief

I think that Butch put it best when he called breast cancer a "mindfuck." Yes! He couldn't have been more on the money. It felt impossible to reconcile all that was happening so fast. Things were out of control. One dose of the chemo medications and the side effects and symptoms had already begun. I was spiraling.

Once again, Butch and Sally were there to save my ass. Butch worked on the physical part and Sally on the mental part. They each understood the other side of the equation, and even though they weren't working together, they did have phone conversations on my behalf to make sure the counterpart was being well managed.

For a while, in addition to targeting and quelling my chemo side effects, I received acupuncture and took a variety of Chinese herbs to target my night sweats, hot flashes, and sluggish memory and cognition. Symptoms were dramatically reduced after a few weeks of consistent sessions. Luckily, the night sweats are now a thing of the past. But the hot flashes have never gone away completely. On the bright side, they've become infrequent and are short-lived. Sometimes, I can predict when they'll strike.

On days when I blow dry my hair, I know that toward the end of the drying process, I'm going to feel a fire building from inside that starts in my abdomen and rolls up to my neck, face, and head until I can't take anymore. I bolt from the steamy bathroom, in whatever I'm wearing (or not), and make a beeline for the balcony off our bedroom. I fling open the door and step out onto the (sometimes snow-covered) balcony. I tilt my head up into the wind and close my eyes. Feeling the air rush through my hair and over my face is magnificent. I've begun building in an extra ten minutes to my routine on these days so that I can have "balcony time." Sometimes the dogs join me. They know I'm not going to chat or pet them. I stand there and breathe. So, they sit and point their snouts up into the wind and breathe as well.

Other times, I have no idea a hot flash is about to surface, and there's little I can do to get relief. One such time is in the car. I will be cruising along in the Montana winter, comfortably tucked into my calf-length down parka, heater cranked. The outside temperature is often in the teens and can be below zero. But when a hot flash comes on, I unzip my coat as far as the seatbelt allows, crank the AC on full blast, and open every window as wide as possible. The dogs love it; my husband, not so much. It's not the ideal solution, but when I'm behind the wheel of the car, it's the best I can manage. What I really want to do is tear off my coat, sweater, shoes, and socks and step out into the snow. It hasn't come to that. Yet.

Hot flashes are not a steady, predictable thing. For a while, after I was seeing Butch regularly, they were next to nonexistent. But when we moved more than one thousand miles away for work (I know, I can't believe I left Butch either), my new state was a hot and steamy inferno and the hot flashes returned with a vengeance. I was getting daily headaches from studying (I was learning German) and other activities like reading, writing, and more-involved thought processes. Without my rock there to work his magic, I looked into options and discovered craniosacral therapy.

If you haven't heard of craniosacral therapy, here's a brief definition from the Cleveland Clinic's website: *"Craniosacral therapy (CST) is a gentle hands-on technique that uses a light touch to examine membranes and movement of the fluids in and around the central*

187

nervous system. The therapist uses gentle pressure techniques to assess the existence of possible disruptions and/or restrictions in your fascial system. Light touch and fascial release may help your muscles and organs naturally relieve stress, which improves function."

I was hopeful that craniosacral therapy would work for me, but I had had no experience and knew no one else personally who did either. I was a guinea pig in my circle. I searched for and found a reputable therapist online and it turned out she worked wonders.

I was convinced when, during a session, I could taste the metal of chemo in my mouth again. My therapist had discovered a pocket of chemo and anesthesia in my system that she was methodically evacuating. In the process of touching my abdomen, her hands turned bright red and burned. She was also met with the horrid taste of metal. She needed frequent breaks to wash her hands and drink water. It took several sessions to empty these last hideouts and rid my body of the chemical residue left behind.

My symptoms dramatically improved, and life was good again.

While hot flashes, night sweats, sleep disruption, and impaired memory had a severe impact on my physical state, I learned that the more I was able to manage these symptoms and not feel overtaken by them, the more my mental state improved.

With Sally's help, and sometimes two sessions per week, I began to accept that menopause and its symptoms were now part of my bigger picture. To survive cancer meant that I was alive and well enough to be dealing with menopause and not more disease. It hasn't been all roses, but given the opportunity to face the symptoms and find ways of dealing with menopause rather than the alternative of not surviving the disease and treatment that spurred its premature presence—well, that's a no-brainer for me. So, I continued to lace up my boots and trudge through the metaphorical snow.

So, What Is Menopause, Really?

Menopause is a phase of a woman's life wherein hormone production declines and she can no longer produce mature eggs. Fairly simple. Totally natural. But simple things aren't always easy, and natural things can bring us to our knees. Without these hormones, the unwelcome and uncomfortable symptoms and potential, and sometimes serious, health risks can permeate.

When it comes to cancer care, not all medications cause early-onset menopause and if they do, for some women, it can reverse. For me, that clearly wasn't the case. That's why I was utterly shocked about a year later when I started to bleed, just like a period. I'd gone hiking with my son and we had about a half-hour drive back home. When I stepped out of the car, I discovered what I thought I'd never see again. Oddly, it felt good. I felt like my body was purging and purifying, as if there were remnants of the last years that needed to go. And so, I bled for about five or six days, it tapered off, and it was gone again.

Then the same thing happened two more times over the following eighteen months. My gynecologist didn't call them periods. She was shocked and worried. After the third time, she recommended some tests to make sure everything was okay. I wasn't worried, but I saw no reason to not verify what my gut was telling me. I had a couple pelvic exams, Pap tests, and a biopsy. When everything came back normal, we all could rest assured that there was nothing to worry about. By then, the bleeding was done for good.

I was just shy of forty-six years old.

What Does Menopause Look Like for Me Now?

- hot flashes (previously night sweats too)
- lowered sex drive
- vaginal dryness
- difficulty maintaining my weight
- difficulty achieving and maintaining muscle tone
- difficulty achieving and maintaining skin tone
- sluggish recall
- difficulty keeping thoughts from "floating away"
- decreased bone density (osteopenia)
- difficulty falling and staying asleep

That's a lot to deal with, but over the last eight years, there are many things that I've tried and still apply to prevent further premature decline:

For hot flashes and night sweats:
- I have had acupuncture, craniosacral therapy, and Chinese herbs to help with the hot flashes and night sweats. Now the night sweats are gone, and the hot flashes are far less frequent and shorter.

For vaginal dryness and lowered sex drive:
- I use a compounded vaginal estriol cream with hyaluronic acid to eliminate vaginal dryness. This also helps with the lowered sex drive. No one looks forward to painful intercourse.
- I investigate and employ creative ways to keep the spark alive.

To maintain my weight:
- I apply more attention to my intake than I previously had to.
- I eat balanced meals that are full of fresh vegetables, fish, chicken, rice, potatoes, or plant-based pasta. I don't eat beef.
- I continue to eat little to no refined sugar. I eat fruit, usually choosing berries and other low-sugar options. I occasionally enjoy honey in my tea or some stevia-sweetened chocolate, but I limit the quantity and frequency.
- I buy organic and unprocessed foods. I grow vegetables and herbs and cook with high-quality oils.
- I consulted with a functional medicine specialist to find out more about my food sensitivities that were triggered by chemo. I now enjoy a gluten-free, dairy-free, and egg-free diet. And yet, I still eat gluten-free, dairy-free, and egg-free ice cream, lasagna, pancakes, and lattes in moderation.

To achieve and maintain skin tone:

- I wear a sunscreen of SPF 50 on my face, neck, and ears every single day. I use SPF 30 on exposed skin when I'm outdoors. When canoeing or paddleboarding, I wear a UPF 50 long-sleeved shirt.
- I use high-quality moisturizer on my face and entire body.
- To exfoliate my skin, I practice dry brushing and use exfoliating cleansers.
- I do face yoga. (Yep, that's a thing.)
- I drink plenty of water to keep my skin and entire body hydrated.

To achieve and maintain muscle tone:

- I do weight-bearing exercises using my own body weight, including yoga postures such as planks (regular and side planks), downward-facing dog, crow pose, and others.

To combat sluggish recall and enhance mental acuity:

- I try new physical things to challenge my body and mind such as cross-country skiing, canoeing, paragliding, and axe throwing.
- I challenge my mind by reading, playing word games, writing a book, taking on new challenges at work, using my hands to create crafts. I cook, garden, go outside as much as possible, and travel. I love to see new places.

For bone health:

- I get regular DEXA scans to understand my bone density and monitor its stability.
- I exercise regularly, especially focusing on upper body strength.
- I drink little to no alcohol and carbonated drinks, which can have a detrimental effect on bone mass.
- Every day, I take vitamins D and K, fish oil, silica, and a supplement that contains calcium, phosphorus, collagen, amino acids, and other elements that make up healthy bone.

- I drink zero caffeine. Caffeine is known to decrease bone mineral density and increase the risk of fracture. This helps with my bone health, but it also helps ensure I'll sleep more soundly.

For my sleep difficulties:
- I take a supplement which helps lower cortisol (the stress hormone) at bedtime.
- I use CBD oil just before bed. About one hundred milligrams in a dropper under the tongue usually does the trick.
- Before bed, I avoid complicated conversations and try to reduce worry by allowing myself "worry time" during the day to think about any topics I think will keep me up at night. Likewise, I avoid any TV or news shows that will activate my stress.
- I read at bedtime to help me drift off.
- I moisturize my feet at bedtime with peppermint foot lotion. It is cooling, comforting, and has the added benefit of keeping my skin soft.
- I keep a large supply of foam ear plugs in my nightstand in case of any extraneous noises that can disrupt my sleep.

For my overall health:
- I take a variety of supplements daily including a vitamin B complex, fiber, CoQ10, magnesium, lutein, zeaxanthin, and probiotics.
- I practice yogic breathing; I dance, sing, play games, watch stand-up comedy, and try my best to take things in stride.

One thing I cannot do is take hormone replacement therapy. Even though the type of cancer I had did not grow in response to estrogen or progesterone (also called ER/PR negative), my doctors do not think that systemic hormone replacement is a smart idea for me. If it is for you, I highly recommend. Like, five stars.

There are other symptoms of menopause that I didn't have, so I can't really address them. As I've said before, not everyone will have the same symptoms or severity, and I don't want to pretend like everyone else's will be like mine. So, I will simply implore you to not take it all lying down or accept that you have to suffer through it all. Treatment is out there. You just have to know where to look. I hope I've given you some clues.

I'm less bothered by actual menopause and the symptoms than I am by the way it was handled by my oncology team. In short, it wasn't. At all. A few sentences about my fertility doesn't even scratch the surface. I hope that patients ask questions, that people get more comfortable with menopause being part of healthy conversation, and that, as a society, we start to demand a more comprehensive approach to women's health care. I believe that the system will change, but only if we change it.

"Like a lotus flower, we too have the ability to rise from the mud, bloom out of the darkness, and radiate into the world."

— Anonymous

Epilogue

On December 17, 2022, I celebrated seven years of health since completing an entire year of cancer-focused treatments. I continue to learn from this experience and understand how to manage my expectations. I had a realization somewhere toward the end of 2022 that I have been enjoying thinking about how many years it has been and am looking forward to saying it's been eight years, then ten years, and beyond. But I took a step back to understand why I've been doing this. I realized that this time buffer feels like a safety buffer. As if the longer I live healthy and free from this disease, the safer I am.

That's nonsense, of course. That line of thinking is causing me to rush through life. I'm striving to live so long and get so much distance from the disease and the experience that my present was suffering.

I am now choosing to remind myself to chill, to live in the moment. The days stack up into months and years in due time, no matter how hard we try to push them forward. I'll get there when I get there, and not a moment too soon.

Progress

In these last seven years, cancer care has been making big strides. For example, the hospital in Bozeman, Montana, is offering integrated medicine with access to nutrition, massage, wound care, and rehab services. And the hospital where I was treated in Denver, Colorado, now offers a variety of resources to survivors and their families. I still believe that there is a long way to go, but it is indeed "going."

I hope that these pages offer something of use to you or someone you love. If so, please pass it on. That's how we make the world a better place.

Much of the later blog I wrote is about my everyday life—which may seem ordinary and mundane. But it was for the ability to continue experiencing my daily life that I fought so hard. Now, after having gone through all that I did, I can see clearly that there's nothing merely "ordinary" about life.

The paragraph that holds the most meaning to me from my blog was written on October 8, 2015. At this point, I was still undergoing immunotherapy infusions and had been finished with radiation therapy for about six weeks. I was writing about expressing gratitude for *everything*, not just the things I wanted but for the things I didn't even know to ask for. I can think of no better way to sum up my experience:

> *I believe that we are presented with challenges in our lives, and until we learn the lessons they are trying to teach, they come back in new and different ways. I know now what I was to learn from cancer. The lessons are almost limitless. One of the most important lessons is that, now, I remember to ask, "Do you know where you're lucky?" And because I got what I needed, I can now say good-bye—and thank you—to cancer.*

Resources

Books with a Focus on Physical and Mental Health and Self-Empowerment

- *Anticancer: A New Way of Life* by David Servan-Schreiber, MD, PhD
- *Staying Well with Guided Imagery* by Belleruth Naparstek
- *Reinventing the Body, Resurrecting the Soul: How to Create a New You* by Deepak Chopra
- *Guiding Yoga's Light: Lessons for Yoga Teachers* by Nancy Gerstein
- *Wild: From Lost to Found on the Pacific Crest Trail* by Cheryl Strayed
- *The Untethered Soul: The Journey Beyond Yourself* by Michael A. Singer
- *Big Magic: Creative Living Beyond Fear* by Elizabeth Gilbert
- *Untamed* by Glennon Doyle
- *WOLFPACK: How to Come Together, Unleash Our Power, and Change the Game* by Abby Wambach
- *Braving the Wilderness: The Quest for True Belonging and the Courage to Stand Alone* by Brené Brown

Websites

NCCAOM – National Certification Commission for Acupuncture and Oriental Medicine: https://www.nccaom.org/find-a-practitioner-directory/.

The Biodynamic Craniosacral Therapy Association of North America BCTA/NA: https://www.craniosacraltherapy.org/find-a-practitioner-page.

Acknowledgments

To Michael: I love you. Always have, always will. Thank you for everything you did and continue to do. I've got another sixty-five-plus years in me, can you bring it?

To Aspen and Zach: I'll always be here for you. Thank you for being there for me. I love you.

To Kerrianne: You kept my shit in a pile when I couldn't. You were there for me, for Michael, for my kids, and for my house. There's never been a finer "sparent" in all the world. We all love you for that.

To Butch and Sally: I honestly don't think I would have survived without you. You kept me alive and well so that I had the strength to complete the oncology treatments. You saved my life, and I consider you friends. Thank you.

To my oncology dream team: You did it. I'm here, I'm healed, and I'm eternally grateful.

To my reconstructive surgeon and his physician assistant and nurse: If you have awards for your work, you totally deserve them.

To my physical therapist, my yoga therapists, my craniosacral therapists, my chiropractor, and my yoga instructors: You rock. Because of you, I feel better, I move freer, and I have a lifelong practice to return to whenever I feel the need to call on it.

To Quique: You were a surprising gift. You blew my mind from beginning to end. I'll always be thankful for your kindness and friendship.

To Dani: You captured my essence in a way I didn't know was possible. Thank you for your vision, your creativity, and your friendship.

To Aaron B., Aaron H., Alex, Ammie, Brittany, Christina, Jennifer, Kara, Kathy, Kris, Leslie, Lisa, Lynelle, Naomi, Patti, and Sue: Thank you for taking me to appointments, for food, for gifts, for friendship, for compassion, for sitting down to drink tea, for advice, for giving so much when I had nothing to give.

To my parents, siblings, sisters-in-law, brothers-in-law, nieces, nephews, cousins, aunts, and uncles: Thank you for your cards, gifts, thoughts, prayers, texts, and more. I kept some of these things in a box that I still have. Even though we live far apart, I felt the love.

To Karen: Even in your absence, your infinite wisdom lives in us.

To the authors who wrote the books that kept me going: Thank you. Please keep writing books.

Don't "expect" ex   to ...
                    or